Assembly (

A Treasury of Fifty Original Stories for Primary School Assembly

Written by
DAVID WEBB

First Published
April 04 in Great Britain by

PUBLISHING

ISBN-10: 1-904374-60-3
ISBN-13: 978-1-904374-60-2

Educational Printing Services Limited
Albion Mill, Water Street, Great Harwood, Blackburn BB6 7QR
Telephone: (01254) 882080   Fax: (01254) 882010
E-mail: enquiries@eprint.co.uk   Website: www.eprint.co.uk

Contents

Story Title	Theme	Page
Signs of Autumn	The Seasons - Autumn	1
Autumn Leaves	The Seasons - Autumn	3
If at First You Don't Succeed...	Perseverance/Determination	6
Helen's Harvest	Harvest	9
Mrs Plumpton's Motor Car	Helping/Good Samaritans	12
The Boastful Tree	Modesty is the best policy	15
Joseph's New School	Coping with change	17
Freddie's Forgetful Friday	Concentration	19
Don't Mess With Fireworks	Firework safety	22
A Foggy Day	The natural world/Weather	25
It's Photograph Day!	School photographs	28
Barry's Bad Lunchtime	Dinnertime behaviour	31
Every Dog has its Day	Caring for pets	34
Cat in the Cold	Caring for pets	37
Twin Trouble	Responsibility/Good organisation	40
The Grumpy Giant	Everyone feels better for a smile	43
It Wasn't Me!	Honesty	46
Leroy's Lies	Honesty	49
A Dozen Cream Cakes	Greed	52
The New Teacher	Appearance can be deceptive	55
Teamwork	Teamwork	57
The Bridge	Teamwork	60
Lucy's Snowman	The Seasons - Winter	63
Winter Days - Lazy Ways	Healthy lifestyle	66
Broken Wings	Consequences/Honesty	69
The Nativity Play	Christmas	72

A Windy Day	The natural world/Weather	74
Our Team's the Best	Loyalty	77
A Faithful Friend	Loyalty	79
Goodbye Mrs Thomson	Loyalty/Retirement	82
Gone Fishing	Managing time	85
Pete's New Friends	Friendship	88
Saving Charlie	Bravery/Courage	91
A Family Day Out	Compromise	94
The Miserable Elf	Be thankful for what you have got	97
Mirror, Mirror on the Wall	Vanity/Learning from mistakes	100
The Two Brothers	Responsibility	103
The Birthday Present	Responsibility	106
The Hare's Revenge	Cheating/Honesty	109
The Day the Rain Came	Water	112
Down on the Farm	Giving and taking advice	115
Danger - Keep Out!	Playing in dangerous places	118
Watching Jenny Wren	The Seasons/Birds in spring	121
Skip to be Fit	Healthy living	123
A Helping Hand	Bullying	126
Too Helpful Harry	Giving help when needed	129
Who Will Help the Lion?	Compassion	132
Teddy Bears Picnic	Teddy bears/Raising funds	135
George and the Ladder	Common sense	137
Butterfly Summer	Butterflies/Nature	140

Signs of Autumn

Theme: The Seasons - Autumn

> **Introduction:** Begin by asking the children which is their favourite season. Ask the children to give reasons for their answers. As each season is mentioned, ask the children what they like about the chosen season. Explain that each season is wonderful and special. You could talk about the fresh, green spring with its new growth and promise of things to come; the wonderful hot summer days and the joy of going on holiday; the clear, crisp, cold winter days with frost and snow - and, of course, the beautiful colours of autumn.

'I don't believe it!' moaned Dad, staring out of the front window, as he munched on a piece of toast at breakfast time. 'I really don't believe it!'

'What's the matter, Dad?' asked Kieran. 'Has your toast gone cold?'

Kieran's father ignored the question and pointed with an accusing finger.

'Just look at my lawn! I spent an hour raking it yesterday and it's completely covered with leaves again!'

'What do you expect?' said Mum, joining her husband at the window. 'It's autumn! That's what happens in autumn - the leaves fall off the trees.'

'I know that,' snapped Dad, 'but I don't see why they have to fall all over my lawn!'

'Don't be so grumpy,' said Mum. 'It's a lovely autumn this year. Just look at the colours of the trees.'

Mum was right. Beyond the bottom of the garden was a farmer's field which was lined with a variety of trees - oak, beech, sycamore and horse chestnut. The colours were spectacular. It had been a hot dry, summer and, as a result, the leaves were even more colourful than usual.

'Wait until it rains,' warned Dad. He was determined to remain grumpy. 'You won't think they're so wonderful when you're slipping and sliding on them and they're blocking the drains.'

Mum gave a resigned sigh and poured out two cups of tea.

'My teacher told us we've got to look out for signs of autumn,' said Kieran, 'so I'm going to tell her all about the hedgehog that visits our garden.'

'Hedgehog?' repeated Dad, looking horrified. 'Awful creatures! All prickly and full of fleas!'

'Take no notice of him,' said Mum. 'Anyway, I've not seen a hedgehog in the garden - tell me about it.'

'I've seen him a few times,' explained Kieran. 'I saw him the other evening at the bottom of the garden near the compost heap. He scurried away when I tried to get near.'

'How do you know it's a 'he'?' asked Dad.

Mum glared at him.

1

'He's really cute,' continued Kieran. 'And then I saw him again yesterday morning. He scurried across the lawn and disappeared under the shed.'

'He's probably getting ready to hibernate for the winter,' said Mum. 'Perhaps he's trying to find the warmest place.'

'I wish I could hibernate for the winter,' grumbled Dad. 'I hate the cold weather.'

'We could go across into Mr. Wright's field, after school,' suggested Mum. 'We should be able to collect seeds from the trees. Look, you can see the sycamore seeds twirling down in the breeze. You can understand why they're called helicopters.'

'Do you know that if you plant them in a pot and leave them outside all winter they will start to grow in spring?' said Dad, joining in at last. 'I can remember when I was a boy I planted some conkers. I watched them grow for years until they got too big for their pots. Eventually, I took them down to the park and gave them to one of the keepers. He let me help him plant them out and do you know what - they're really big trees now and they form conkers themselves!'

'I'd love to do that!' said Kieran, enthusiastically. 'Will you come and help me collect some after school, Dad?'

'I'll get some pots out of the shed so that we can plant them,' said Dad. 'We'll see if we can collect some acorns and beech nuts as well. We can do an experiment and see which seeds germinate and grow the best.'

'Thanks, Dad,' said Kieran. 'I can't wait!'

Kieran sipped his mug of hot tea and stared out of the window at the autumn scene. The russet leaves drifted and swirled in the morning breeze; a few wisps of white cloud drifted across the clear blue sky and, just as Dad turned away, the garden hedgehog came out from beneath the shed and scurried across the lawn before disappearing into the next door neighbour's garden.

'Signs of autumn,' thought Kieran. 'Autumn really is a lovely season!'

Prayer: Thank you, Lord, for autumn time. Thank you for the beautiful colours and the swirling twirling leaves; thank you for the cold mornings and autumn mists; thank you for the farmers who gather in their autumn harvest and thank you for the birds and animals which busily prepare for winter. Thank you, Lord, for autumn time. Amen.

Follow up: Talk about autumn seeds. The children are sure to be able to bring in a variety of seeds they collect - beech nuts, sycamore seeds, acorns, conkers etc. Plant a selection of the seeds in different pots and find a place to leave them outside until spring. (Make a note in your diary to check them!)

Look at the seeds in different autumn fruits - e.g. plums, apples, blackberries, pears etc. These can also be grown in pots and can be kept indoors. It is a good idea to soak the seeds overnight before planting. You could even hold a competition to see which child can produce the best plant from an autumn seed!

2

Autumn Leaves

Theme: The Seasons - Autumn

> **Introduction:** This assembly is best used on a crisp, clear autumn day. Begin by talking generally about autumn. Ask the children if they can tell you some of the things that happen in autumn (falling leaves, birds migrate, shorter days etc.). Talk about the lovely autumn colours. Have a few different leaves to show the children. Look at the different shapes of the leaves and identify each one. Explain that some trees are deciduous and some are evergreen. See if they can name an evergreen tree. Ask the children if they know why some trees lose their leaves as winter approaches.

It was early October and the first real frost of autumn sparkled on the grass in the bright morning sunlight.

'I'm glad you put the heating on,' said Emma. She was sitting at the breakfast table staring out of the back window. 'It looks freezing out there.'

'It looks lovely,' replied her mum, pouring a cup of steaming tea. 'I love bright autumn days.'

'You're lucky to have central heating,' chipped in Emma's gran. 'When I was a little girl I used to wake up on a cold frosty morning to frost patterns all over my bedroom window. Sometimes I could see my breath it was that cold!'

Emma's gran was always telling her what it was like when she was a child. Emma smiled politely and gazed out of the window. A few golden leaves drifted onto the lawn from the huge sycamore tree beyond the garden fence. A sycamore seed spun gracefully to the ground like a helicopter coming in to land.

'We're collecting leaves in the school grounds today,' said Emma, sipping her hot tea. 'We're doing an autumn project and we need different types of leaves.'

'I used to collect leaves when I was a little girl,' announced gran. 'It's nice to know that some things don't change!'

Later that day, after lunch, Emma's class lined up by the school door ready. One or two children had to be sent back to get their coats. It was a beautiful bright afternoon but Mrs Harris, Emma's teacher, explained that although it looked lovely there was a chill autumn wind.

'Now I want you to work in twos,' explained Mrs Harris, as the children gathered at the bottom of the school field. 'There are lots of different trees around the school field and I want you to collect as many different leaves as possible. You'll probably find some acorns and beech nuts as well. When we get back into class we'll have a good look at our collections. Now find a partner and off you go!'

Emma chose to work with her best friend Usma and the two girls set off across the school field.

There was an obvious starting place. A huge oak tree dominated one corner of the field and the two girls decided to gather some oak leaves - after all, their school was called Oak Tree Primary School.

'It looks so old,' said Emma, as they stood beneath the spreading branches. 'I wonder how long it's been here.'

'It looks even older than Mrs Harris,' giggled Usma. She rubbed her hands against the gnarled bark. 'It's more wrinkled too!'

A familiar voice suddenly sounded from behind the two girls. 'Thanks for that, Usma. I'm glad I'm not as wrinkled as an old oak tree!'

Mrs Harris was smiling but Usma's face had turned bright red.

The girls collected their oak leaves, gathered up some acorns and then continued their search. A little further around the field a beautiful red beech tree stood proudly, a shower of leaves drifting down to the ground every so often. There were beech nuts too, bursting out of their casings like little brown gems. Emma and Usma had not realised that there were so many different trees in the school grounds. For most of the school year they took the trees for granted. They offered shade from the hot summer sun but they were definitely at their best in autumn.

At one point the girls had to run away from a group of boys who showered them with sycamore leaves - until Mrs Harris's angry voice put a stop to their game! As soon as the teacher turned her back the boys pulled faces and raced off across the field towards their favourite horse chestnut tree.

By the time the children were called together, the two girls had a bag full of lovely different coloured leaves.

'Splendid!' announced Mrs Harris. 'We will be able to learn so much from our collections and I'm sure we can think of some good ideas for autumn art work. Now let's take our collections back into school and have a proper look at them, should we?'

A sudden gust of wind made Emma shiver. She had really enjoyed her afternoon collecting leaves - but she was looking forward to snuggling up in bed later that evening - especially if the central heating was on.

Prayer: Thank you, Lord, for the beautiful season of autumn. Thank you for the lovely colours of the autumn fruits and leaves. Thank you for the crisp, clear days and the cold autumn nights. May we learn to love and appreciate the wonder of the changing seasons. Amen.

Follow up: An obvious follow up is to ask the children to collect autumn leaves. To avoid a forest of leaves, explain that they should just collect one of each type! Look at and identify the different leaves.
Use a sheet of A3 paper to produce a collage of leaf rubbings. The children should choose coloured crayons, either wax or pencil, as near to the leaf colour as possible.

Encourage the children to look at the distinctive shapes of the different trees and, where possible, to make observational drawings.

Autumn, with its wonderful colours, is a splendid subject for poetry. Finished poems lend themselves well to illustration and can be used both for presentation in assembly and for display.

If at First You Don't Succeed...

Theme: Perseverance/Determination

Introduction: Explain to the children that not everything in life will come easy to them. Sometimes you have to persevere and be very determined if you are going to succeed. For example, you might, at first, find it difficult to swim or to ride a bicycle. You could just give up but if you persevere and practise you could have a hobby that could last a lifetime. Sometimes, you might struggle with your work at school. However, if you persevere and try really hard your understanding increases and the work gradually becomes easier.

We can often learn a great deal from nature and the creature in today's story can teach us a valuable lesson about perseverance.

Hairy spider lived in a big, spiky bush at the bottom of the garden. Throughout the long, hot summer she had kept away from all the other creatures that had invaded the garden. She had avoided the birds and the family cat, she had hidden from the hedgehog that came out each night and, most of all, she had managed to keep clear of those awful house children. They were the worst of the creatures - always charging around and causing chaos. It was a dangerous world for a garden spider!

Now it was autumn and it was time for hairy spider to weave her web. She began on a clear, calm evening when the children had disappeared inside and the house cat was fast asleep. Firstly, she explored the spiky bush and chose her spot carefully. It was perfect - about half way up the bush and facing the garden fence. Hairy spider got to work. She spun her delicate, silky threads and attached the framework to the spiky bush. Backwards and forwards, up and down, round and round she worked tirelessly until the beautiful orb web began to take shape. But there was a problem. As she had been working the weather had begun to change. The clear sky had gradually been replaced by storm clouds and a fierce wind had blown up, whipping the autumn leaves into a frenzy.

Hairy spider clung to her web as the spiky bush swayed to and fro. It smashed against the wooden fence but still the little spider clung hold. Her web was strong and she was determined her hard work would not be in vain. The rain lashed down and the storm worsened. Suddenly, a terrific gust of wind caught the bush and sent it crashing against the fence. The web was torn apart, hairy spider lost her grip and she tumbled to the cold, wet ground, clinging to one last silky thread.

By the following morning, the storm had subsided. The tired spider had climbed back into the safety of the spiky bush and, after a brief rest, she began her work

all over again. Slowly, patiently, she weaved her silky threads until the orb web once again began to take shape. She had almost finished when the garden was filled with noise. Those two awful house children had come out to play. Hairy spider could see them through her eight eyes. She continued her work, hoping that they would keep well away from the spiky bush.

'Let's play football!' shouted Josh, and he belted the ball down the garden and into the empty net that his dad had put up for him.

'I'm not going in goal!' replied his younger brother Sam. 'The grass is too wet after the storm. I'm not getting covered in mud!'

'Let's kick it against the fence, then,' suggested Josh, and he picked the ball out of the net and kicked it towards the wooden fence at the bottom of the garden.

The heavy ball flew through the air and crashed into the spiky bush, completely destroying the delicate spider web. Once more, hairy spider was thrown to the ground where she scrambled away and hid near the bottom of the bush.

'Forget it!' shouted Sam. 'The grass is too wet. I'm going back inside.'

Stunned by the force of the football, it took hairy spider an hour to recover. Gradually, she climbed back up the spiky bush until she had reached the remnants of her orb web. Should she give up - or should she try again? There was no doubt in her mind. Hairy spider set to work, patiently spinning and weaving her gossamer threads until the wonderful web stretched across the spiky branches and glistened in the late evening sunshine. Completely exhausted by her hard work, hairy spider crawled to the centre of her web and rested.

The house cat crept past on its regular evening hunt for mice - but it didn't disturb hairy spider. The grown ups took a stroll down the garden, just to get some fresh air after their evening meal - but they didn't disturb hairy spider. It was only when the two children charged down after their parents that spider opened her eyes in panic - but there was no need.

'Hey!' exclaimed Josh, pointing towards the shimmering silky web. 'Take a look at that! It's fantastic!'

'Yes, it is,' agreed the grown ups. 'Just think of all the hard work that has gone into weaving that beautiful web. We'll have to be very careful not to damage it, won't we?'

'Yes, we certainly will!' thought hairy spider, and she closed her eight eyes and drifted into peaceful sleep.

Prayer: Lord, we can learn so much from nature. Help us to appreciate the wonderful world that you have created. Help us to care for the birds and the animals and the insects. May we never do anything to harm the creatures that share our world. Amen.

7

Follow up: Spiders are fascinating creatures. Set the children a task (it could be a voluntary homework task) to find out all they can about spiders. Encourage them to produce illustrated fact sheets or small booklets about spiders. Different groups of children could research different types of spiders - e.g. house spiders, jumping spiders, poisonous spiders.

The best time to go spider hunting is autumn. The children are sure to find examples of spiders in the school grounds. It is better to **observe** rather than touch and disturb. If magnifying glasses are available the children will be able to distinguish the different parts of the spider.

Helen's Harvest

Theme: Harvest

Introduction: Ask the children if they can tell you why Harvest is always celebrated in autumn. Explain that Harvest Festivals are always held at the time of year when crops are gathered in. The summer sun has ripened the crops in the fields or the fruit on the trees and they have to be gathered in before they are damaged by the winter frosts. Harvest services are held to thank God for both the harvest of the land and the harvest of the sea. Harvest also provides an opportunity for us to remember how lucky we are and to give to those who are less fortunate.

'I don't understand why we have a harvest assembly at school,' said Helen, as she placed a tin of peas into her shoe box. 'What's the point of it?'

Helen's mum paused for thought. She remembered her own school days, when she would collect fresh vegetables from her father's garden and set them on straw in a wicker basket. 'It's to thank God for providing us with food for the year,' explained mum. 'The farmers gather their crops in autumn and so we hold harvest festivals. Not everyone is as lucky as us, you know. Even in this country some people struggle for food and there are a lot of places far worse off.'

'But we could hold a harvest assembly at any time,' persisted Helen. 'We're taking in tins and packets. We get those from the supermarket, not the farmers!'

'It wasn't always like that,' said mum. 'In fact, it's not that long ago that there were no supermarkets. When I was a little girl we always used to take fresh fruit or vegetables. My dad had turned most of our back garden into a vegetable patch. I used to pack a basket with my mum. Do you know, I can still smell the fresh food if I close my eyes and imagine.'

'That sounds much better than a load of tins and packets,' said Helen, staring into her shoe box. 'I wish I could take fresh vegetables.'

'Oh, there's a place for tins and packets,' said mum. 'They're much more convenient. But you know, there's nothing to stop you growing your own crops for next year then you could gather your harvest just like the farmers.'

Helen's eyes lit up. What a great idea. She would ask for her own patch of garden and grow her very own food to harvest.

The months passed and Helen's mum had forgotten all about their harvest conversation. Her time was taken up with Christmas preparations and Helen's birthday was in February. It came as quite a surprise when, at the beginning of March, Helen suddenly asked, 'When do I start getting my patch ready for harvest?'

'Harvest?' repeated mum, looking surprised. 'It's the beginning of spring, Helen. Harvest is in autumn!'

9

'Exactly,' said Helen. 'It's the beginning of spring and the gardening man on television said it was time to start sowing seeds.'

Helen's mum laughed. 'Well, I suppose the gardening man knows best!' she said. 'We'd better see what we can sort out for you.'

That very weekend Helen and her mum and dad went into the back garden to mark out a patch. The ground was still very damp and the soil was heavy but they agreed that a rectangle of ground behind the shed could be Helen's garden. It was hard work digging and it took a good hour to turn over the soil and hoe the clumps to break them up.

'You can't really sow anything into the open ground yet,' explained dad. 'We're still getting frost at nights and any young seedlings wouldn't survive.'

Helen looked disappointed. She was eager to get started.

'Don't worry,' said dad. 'We can sow some seeds in pots. That will give them a good start and we can plant them in a few weeks.'

They went to the local garden centre and bought a variety of seeds - carrots, cabbage, runner beans and broad beans. They also bought some seed potatoes and onion sets.

'We won't have room for much more,' explained dad. 'Your patch will be pretty crowded as it is.'

Helen had fun planting the seeds into pots. She had to wait a couple of weeks to put the potatoes in but it was not long before fresh green shoots began to push through the brown earth. Helen felt so proud! She watered and weeded her patch and looked at it every day - even when it was raining. The shoots grew into young plants and throughout the summer, the young plants got stronger and stronger. Helen watched the runner beans flower, clusters of red on tall green stems. She was so excited when the young beans began to form. She was a little worried when her potato plants started to wither and brown but dad explained that the potatoes were underneath the ground and that it was quite natural for the tops to die.

September passed and Helen brought home a letter from school containing details of the harvest assembly.

'Fantastic!' she said. 'I've been waiting a whole year for this!'

It was so exciting gathering in her own harvest. Of course, she only picked what she needed but her harvest basket was full to overflowing - and there was still plenty left for the family to enjoy.

'I must admit,' said mum, as the two of them stood and admired the vegetable patch, 'I've quite enjoyed watching your harvest grow this year. Shall we do it again?'

'Of course we'll do it again!' said Helen. 'From now on I'm going to grow my own harvest every year!'

Prayer: Thank you, Lord, for harvest time. Thank you for the farmers who work so hard to produce their crops. Thank you for the fishermen who risk their lives to trawl the seas. Thank you for the sun and rain that make the crops grow. Thank you for the wonderful cycle of nature that brings us harvest time. Thank you, Lord. Amen.

Follow up: An ideal follow up would be to get the children to plant some seeds. Perhaps it would be possible to develop a small area within the school grounds. If not, plant in pots. Even seed potatoes can be planted in a large pot and grown in a classroom or outbuilding.

Look at the seeds in various fruits. Apple or orange pips are easy to grow and make attractive plants, if cared for properly. Soak the pips overnight before planting. A plastic bag over the pot helps germination.

Mrs Plumpton's Motor Car

Theme: Good Samaritans

> **Introduction:** No matter how independent you are there will come a time when you need help. You might need help from a doctor if you become ill; you might need help from a dentist if your teeth need attention; you might need help from your teacher if you get stuck with your school work. Usually there is someone you can turn to for help but the person in today's story received help from a most unexpected source.

Mrs Plumpton was seventy-eight years old and still as fit as a fiddle. She still lived in her own house, did all her own cooking and cleaning and tended her own garden in which she grew a variety of vegetables as well as pretty flowers. Mrs Plumpton was fiercely proud of her independence and she was particularly proud of the fact that she could still drive her little car - a bright red Ford Fiesta that she had owned for the best part of twenty years. Twice a week she drove to the supermarket to do her own shopping and each Sunday she drove to her local church, stopping to collect her friend Mrs Gregson on the way. Everybody who knew her agreed that Mrs Plumpton was a very proud and determined lady.

It came as a pleasant surprise when, late one evening, she received a phone call from her sister Annie who lived some twenty miles away.

'Will you come over next weekend and stay for a couple of nights?' said Annie. 'It's my birthday and I'm having a bit of a get together. I'll pay for your taxi. It won't be a problem.'

'You'll do no such thing!' insisted Mrs Plumpton. 'I've never taken a taxi in my life and I'm not going to start now! I'll drive over as I always do, thank you very much!'

And she did. The very next Saturday morning Mrs Plumpton set off bright and early, her old brown suitcase packed into the boot of her little Ford Fiesta, next to the present she had bought for her sister. It was a dull day and the threat of rain did not look too far away. Although she would never admit it to her sister, Mrs Plumpton was a little bit nervous about the journey, especially the part that took her across the open moorland. It was such a lonely stretch of road and the bleak moor had never been one of Mrs Plumpton's favourite places. Still, in less than an hour she would be safe and sound with her sister.

The first sign of trouble came as she drove along the steep approach road to the moor. It had just begun to rain, large droplets falling from a dark grey sky. Mrs Plumpton's Fiesta spluttered and jerked as it lost power. It picked up for a moment but then it spluttered again. Mrs Plumpton pressed harder on the accelerator but the engine cut out completely and the car rolled to a halt on the long, straight,

deserted moorland road.

'I don't believe it!' she said aloud, staring at the dead instrument panel. 'It's never let me down before! What a good job I'm a member of the RAC.'

She nodded in satisfaction for a moment and then realised that she had no way of contacting them. She did not have a mobile phone. She hated them - always going off in public places - playing silly annoying tunes. She sat in her little car watching the raindrops trickle down her windscreen and she wished she'd listened to her nephew and bought herself a mobile phone.

There was nothing else for it - she would just have to wait until another car came along the road and she would ask for help.

She did not have to wait long. She saw the dipped headlights first in her rear view mirror and then the blue van came into sight. It was a Smithson's van - a local firm that Mrs Plumpton had used on several occasions. Mrs Plumpton rolled down her window and waved her handkerchief so that the driver would see she was in trouble. The blue van picked up speed and raced straight past.

'Well fancy that!' exclaimed Mrs Plumpton, talking out loud again. 'That's the last time I use that firm! Wait until I see Mr Smithson!'

Ten minutes later another vehicle approached. This time it was a car and it seemed to be travelling quite slowly. Good! It couldn't miss her. To make sure, Mrs Plumpton got out of her Fiesta and stood at the side of the road in full view of the approaching car. She spotted a man and a lady in the two front seats and there seemed to be a couple of children in the back. Mrs Plumpton waved her handkerchief wildly. The car slowed for a moment, one of the children pulled a face and then the car picked up speed and disappeared into the distance.

Mrs Plumpton stood there with her mouth open, staring at the car until it vanished over a ridge. What was wrong with people? Why didn't they stop to help?

Half an hour passed and Mrs Plumpton was beginning to feel desperate. The sky was darker than ever and the rain was lashing down. She was cold too. The engine was completely dead and so the heater didn't work. There was only one thing for it - she would have to get out and walk, even if it was miles across the moor to the next village. Mrs Plumpton pulled up the collar on her coat, opened the car door and set off along the lonely moorland road.

She had not gone far when she saw a vehicle heading towards her. That was no good, it was going the wrong way. Besides, it was full of youths wearing baseball caps and playing loud music. She stood to the side so that she wasn't drowned by the spray of the passing car. To her surprise, the vehicle slowed down and stopped alongside her. The driver lowered his window and a particularly loud piece of rap music belted out. He killed the sound and then he spoke.

'What's up, Mrs? Are you in a spot of trouble?'

'My car's broken down,' explained Mrs Plumpton, approaching the driver's window. 'I was on my way to see my sister when the engine cut out. I don't suppose you could phone the RAC for me, could you? I don't own a mobile myself.'

'Of course I will,' said the driver, giving her a beaming smile. 'But it could be a while before anyone arrives to look at your car. I'll tell you what - you climb in the back and I'll turn the car around and deliver you to your sister. My mate Eddie will wait with your car until the RAC arrive. How does that sound?'

'Well, if you're absolutely sure . . .' said Mrs Plumpton, as the rear door opened and Eddie stepped out. 'That really is very kind of you!'

'No problem!' said the driver. 'We'll soon have you safe and sound. My name's Leroy, by the way. Tell you what - you look a cool kind of Granny - we'll listen to some rap music on the way to your sister's!'

Half an hour later, Annie, Mrs Plumpton's sister, stood at her front door and stared in amazement as Mrs Plumpton emerged from the back of a very noisy car. Leroy held the door open for her and Mrs Plumpton beamed in gratitude.

'Thank you ever so much,' shouted Mrs Plumpton. 'And great music, by the way.'

'Right on!' said Leroy, and he raised his hand and grinned from ear to ear. 'High fives, Mrs P!'

'High fives!' returned Mrs Plumpton.

Annie's mouth dropped open as Leroy's car sped out of sight.

'It's a long story,' began Mrs Plumpton. 'Let's go inside and I'll tell you all about it!'

Prayer: Help us, Lord, to judge people not by the way they look but by the deeds they do. May we learn to be responsible and considerate citizens who will always be ready to help those in need. May we listen to your teaching and always be prepared to be good Samaritans. Amen.

Follow up: Discuss with the children why they think firstly the van and then the family car failed to stop and help Mrs Plumpton. Why did Mrs Plumpton not expect the car full of youths to stop and help?

Read the story of *The Good Samaritan* from The Bible and draw the obvious comparison.

Discuss ways in which the children can act as 'Good Samaritans' in and around school.

14

The Boastful Tree

Theme: Modesty is the best policy

> **Introduction:** Begin by asking the children: 'Do you like people who are always boasting? Do you like people who are always showing off because they think they are better than everybody else?' Explain that there are lots of talented people in the world. One person might be good at sport while another is good at music; one person might be good at maths while another person can draw wonderful pictures. However, no matter how talented you are, it is better to leave someone else to sing your praises. If you boast too much you might just find that you are not as wonderful as you think you are!

Two proud trees stood on the side of a grassy hill enjoying the warm autumn sunshine. The tall sycamore swayed in the gentle breeze while the little evergreen fir tree looked down on the surrounding countryside in quiet satisfaction.

'Just look at me,' began the sycamore, as a few golden yellow leaves floated to the floor. 'Don't I look beautiful in autumn? My leaves change to such lovely colours - golds, reds and yellows - while you stay the same boring green colour all the year round. I'm glad I'm not an evergreen tree, I wouldn't like to be so dull.'

The little fir tree looked up at his towering neighbour and had to agree that the sycamore looked splendid. 'I suppose my pine needles are a bit boring,' she thought to herself, 'but I should be satisfied with what I've got. After all, not everyone can be as beautiful as the sycamore.'

'And just look at my seeds,' continued the sycamore. 'How lovely they look swirling and twirling in the autumn breeze - much prettier than your silly fir cones. Yes, I really am a splendid specimen, aren't I?'

The little fir tree did not answer so the sycamore started again.

'Come to think of it, I'm much more interesting in spring than you are. Oh, I know you perk up a little bit and you do your best to grow but you don't burst into life with beautiful spring green buds, do you? And then in summer - I'm covered in luscious leaves that offer shade and shelter from the hot summer sun while you stand there looking just the same as ever! I'm so beautiful that I almost feel sorry for you!'

The little fir tree could not think of anything to say in reply and so she kept quiet - but inside she was feeling sad and wishing that she had lovely colourful leaves that floated and drifted in the autumn breeze.

The weeks passed by and the bright autumn sunshine disappeared to be replaced by bitter easterly winds. Swirling mists enveloped the hillside and morning frosts turned the countryside crystal white. The tall sycamore was completely stripped of its leaves and it stood shivering, silhouetted against the cold sky.

'I d-d-don't really like this t-t-time of year,' stuttered the sycamore. 'I w-w-wish it were w-w-warmer!'

'Winter's only just beginning,' warned the little fir tree. 'Wait until the snow and ice gets a grip!'

'It's n-n-not fair!' stammered the jealous sycamore. 'You're still c-c-covered in pine needles and I've lost my c-coat!'

'But it was only a few weeks ago that you were boasting about how beautiful you were,' reminded the little fir tree. 'You told me I was dull and boring!'

A mass of grey clouds had gathered above the hillside and the first few flakes of snow had begun to flutter gently to the ground.

'Oh, no!' groaned the sycamore. 'It's snowing! I hate the snow! It makes me feel so cold!'

'I love the snow!' enthused the little fir tree. 'It sticks to my needles and it makes my fir cones shine like jewels!'

'It's not fair!' repeated the envious sycamore. 'I don't see why I have to lose all my leaves just as we get to the coldest time of the year! I wish I was an evergreen tree like you!'

'Perhaps you should be satisfied with what you've got?' suggested the little fir tree. 'Why don't you have a long rest until springtime and you can dream about how lucky you are and I'll stand here and enjoy the beautiful crisp winter?'

'Yes, I think I'll do that,' agreed the shivering sycamore. 'And perhaps when I wake up in spring I won't show off quite the same.'

The little fir tree smiled to herself as the snow fell more heavily and settled on her branches. 'We'll wait and see,' she thought. 'We'll wait and see!'

Prayer: Lord, make us kind and thoughtful people who never do or say anything that may hurt or offend others. Let us not be boastful or conceited but help us to use our talents wisely for the good of others. May we live our lives by following your example. Amen.

Follow up: Ask the children to research the difference between evergreen and deciduous trees, finding examples of both.

'Trees in winter' is a good topic for art work. Get the children to paint silhouetted trees against a washed background. They can experiment with different colours for the wash (e.g. different shades of blue or reds, yellows, orange etc.).

Joseph's New School

Theme: Coping with change

> **Introduction:** Tell the children about something from your experience that you were not looking forward to but that did not turn out to be as bad as you thought. For example, it could be a visit to the dentist, a stay in hospital or even an OFSTED inspection! Ask the children for their own experiences. Ask: 'Has anyone ever worried about moving up into a new class or about meeting a new teacher?' Explain that the boy in today's story was worried about moving to a new school - but, with the help of a few kind people, he soon settled in and began to enjoy the experience.

Joseph stood at the school gate and stared with trepidation into the crowded playground. It was his first day at St. John's Primary School and he was feeling really nervous. He had forced some breakfast down but now his stomach was churning and he was beginning to wish he hadn't bothered. He had waved goodbye to his mum at the bottom of the street. She had wanted to deliver him into the playground but there was no way he was going to let the other children see him arrive at his new school holding his mum's hand. He was in Year 5, after all! What he didn't know was that his mum was still waiting, just out of sight around the corner, determined to see that he got into school safely.

Why did he have to move school? It was his father's fault! He had got promotion at work but it meant that the family had to move area and it was just too far for Joseph to travel to his old school. He had been so happy at Hutton Street. He had been coping well with his lessons, he had lots of really good friends and he had even come on as a substitute for the school football team on a couple of occasions. Now he would have to start all over again. He didn't know anyone and he was worried that he might not have covered the same work as the other children. Joseph looked around forlornly. He was beginning to wish that his mum was still with him.

A football thumped against the school gate and a boy with fair hair and freckles ran across to retrieve it.

    'Are you the new boy?' he asked, picking the ball up and staring at Joseph. 'Mrs Harris said a new boy was joining our class.'

    'Well, I am starting today,' stammered Joseph, doing his best to smile. 'I'm going into Year 5.'

    'That's our class,' confirmed the fair haired boy. Two of his friends had strolled across to join him. 'My Name's Josh,' said the boy, opening the gate. 'And this is Daniel - and this is Stephen.'

    Joseph stepped into the playground. He was feeling a little more relaxed

17

and confident. 'I'm Joe,' he said. 'I don't really know anyone around here.'

'Just hang around with us,' said Daniel. 'You'll soon settle in.'

A group of Year 5 girls wandered across to take a look at the new boy. A couple of them pointed and giggled.

'Take no notice of them,' said Josh. 'You stick with us and you'll be all right.'

'Are you any good at football?' asked Stephen. 'We could do with another good player for our team.'

'I played for my last school team a couple of times,' explained Joseph. 'Only as a substitute, mind you.'

'Great!' said Josh, kicking the ball into the air. 'Let's see what you can do, then!'

By the time the bell rang to mark the start of the school day, Josh was feeling much better. His mum was also feeling better. Seeing him playing with a group of friends, she had wandered off to do some shopping. The children lined up and the duty teacher came out into the yard to supervise the classes walking into school.

'That's Mrs Harris, our teacher,' whispered Daniel, who was lined up alongside Joseph. 'She looks a bit fierce but she's all right really.'

'I heard that, Daniel Moore!' snapped the teacher, glaring along the line. 'Still, I suppose it's nice to know I'm all right, really!' She walked along the line and stopped next to Joseph. 'You must be Joseph?' she said, in a softer voice. 'I see you've made a few friends already.'

'Yes, thank you, Mrs Harris,' replied Joseph, a little nervously.

'Well that's good,' said Mrs Harris, clasping her hands together. 'We want you to feel at home nice and quickly. There are a lot of lovely children in our class and I think you'll really like it at St. John's School.' She beamed down at Joseph for a few seconds and then returned to the front of the line. 'Now then, Year 5! Move in quietly, please!'

'Yes, I think I am going to like it,' thought Joseph as he made his way into school. 'I really think I am going to like it here!'

Prayer: Lord, give us confidence and determination when we are faced with a new challenge. Sometimes we may feel nervous when we have to face a new situation. We all have to face changes in our lives but we know that you are alongside us, that you are there with us, guarding us and guiding us. Amen.

Follow up: Ask the children to try and imagine how Joseph must have been feeling as he waited outside the school gates. Write down the words or phrases that the children give you. Discuss how they would feel if they had to move to a completely new area. What would they miss? Remind them what they should do if a new pupil joins the school. Stress how important it is to make anyone new to the school feel really welcome.

18

Freddie's Forgetful Friday

Theme: Concentration

> **Introduction:** Explain to the children that sometimes as people grow older they become a little forgetful. Some people become forgetful because they do not keep their brains active enough; some people become forgetful because they do so much that they just have too many things to remember! However, some people - even children - become forgetful because they can not be bothered to remember things that could be very important.
>
> Today's story is about a boy who was so obsessed with playing in the first match of the season for his football team that he forgot about quite a few things that were very important.

It was Friday and Freddie couldn't wait for the school day to be over. You see, the following morning - Saturday - Freddie was playing his very first football match for his new team, Brenton Rovers. He was so excited that he forgot to have a wash or clean his teeth before he set off for school. The result was that a rather grubby boy turned up in class that Friday morning and some of the other children pulled a face when they saw him.

'It's not my fault,' explained Freddie, as Emily Parkinson edged away from him. 'I'll have a wash this evening before I go to bed!'

Freddie's teacher, Mr Schofield, noticed that there was something wrong. Firstly, Freddie forgot to answer when his name was called out for the register and then, when his friend Ben nudged him in the ribs, he spluttered, 'Yes, mum!' much to the amusement of the rest of the class.

'I'm certainly not your mum,' asserted Mr Schofield, peering over his glasses. 'And when did you last comb your hair, boy? You look as if you've been dragged through a hedge backwards!'

The morning did not get any better. After assembly, Mr Schofield collected in the homework - but Freddie had forgotten to do his.

'I'm sorry, Sir, I've left it at home,' lied Freddie. 'I was in a bit of a rush this morning and I'm excited about my football match tomorrow.'

'It's not a problem,' smiled Mr Schofield, and then he glared at Freddie and added, 'You can stay in this playtime and do it again!'

Freddie frowned and fumbled in his pocket for his handkerchief - which he had forgotten to bring.

Once the homework had been collected in it was time for the weekly spelling test. Freddie looked around nervously. His spelling list was still in his tray, where he had placed it on Monday morning. He had forgotten to take it home and he hadn't a clue how to spell most of the words on the list. He tried to sneak a

look at Emily's answers but she covered her paper with her hand and edged still further away from him. Freddie scored three out of twenty and, when the papers were collected in, he made sure his was on the bottom of the pile so that Mr Schofield would get to it last of all.

Freddie was relieved when dinner time arrived. However, his relief turned to despair when he realised he'd forgotten his lunch box. He fumbled in his pocket and pulled out a brown banana skin and a bit of half eaten cheese. The cheese was a bit hairy but he nibbled it anyway until his friend Ben took pity on him and gave him one of his ham sandwiches.

'Thanks for the sandwich,' said Freddie. 'I'm just a bit excited about the match tomorrow. I don't usually forget things.'

Ben grunted and got on with his lunch. It was the third day that week he'd given Freddie one of his sandwiches.

Freddie got through the afternoon reasonably well despite the fact that he couldn't find his sketch book for the art lesson. It was only when he was half way home that he realised he'd left his coat in the school cloakroom.

'Never mind,' he said to himself. 'It'll still be there on Monday. I won't need a coat for the football match tomorrow morning.'

Ten minutes later he arrived home to find the house locked and no one in. It was then that he remembered he was supposed to go to his Gran's house straight after school! Not to worry, she was used to him turning up late!

Freddie was glad to climb into bed that night. At least when he was asleep he couldn't forget anything! He turned out his bedside lamp and within minutes he had drifted off into a deep, dreamless sleep.

He woke up with a start the following morning. His mum was shaking his arm roughly and when he opened his eyes she had the telephone in her hand.

'It's your football coach,' she whispered, her hand covering the mouthpiece. 'He doesn't sound very pleased!'

Freddie rubbed his eyes and grabbed the phone. 'Yes, coach?' he said, sleepily. 'Is there a problem?'

'I'll say there's a problem!' barked Freddie's football coach. 'The problem is you, Freddie! You're not here, are you! We're twenty minutes into the match and we're two goals down because we're a player short!'

Freddie gasped and looked towards his alarm clock. It was ten-thirty! He'd forgotten to set the alarm before he went to sleep! 'I - I'm sorry, coach,' he stammered, scrambling out of bed. 'I'm on my way! I can be there in ten minutes!'

'Don't bother,' snapped the coach. 'You'd probably get lost, anyway! If you remember to turn up for training mid week, perhaps we'll think again!'

Freddie sank back onto the bed and held his head in his hands. From that moment on he made a resolution that no longer would he be Forgetful Freddie. Only time would tell if he would be able to keep it.

Prayer: Lord, may we grow up to be reliable and dependable citizens. Make us realise that it is often important to remember things so that we remain safe and healthy and so that we do not let other people down. Teach us self discipline and responsibility. Amen.

Follow up: Ask the children if they have ever forgotten anything important. Discuss the consequences.

Talk in more detail about why it is important to remember things learned at school such as: how to read, write and be proficient at numeracy; road safety lessons; health education lessons etc.

Don't Mess With Fireworks

Theme: Firework safety

Introduction: Used a week or so before Bonfire Night, this story reinforces messages about firework safety. In particular, it reminds children about the danger of playing with fireworks. Begin by asking the children if any of them are going to have their own fireworks on Bonfire Night. Ask who is going to set off the fireworks and see if the children can give you the safety rules for Bonfire Night. Explain that fireworks are not toys and that they can be very dangerous particularly if they are misused.

Joe's mum had warned him to keep away from Andy and his friends.

'He'll get you into trouble,' she had said. 'He's three years older than you and he's already been in bother at school. Take my advice for once and stay away from him!'

Joe had listened for a while but Andy and his friends were such good fun. O.K. - he was a bit streetwise but Joe didn't mind that. In fact, it was a good thing to learn to stand up for yourself. Besides, none of Joe's school friends lived near enough for him to play with them and so it was convenient to hang around with Andy.

After he had finished his homework one Monday night in early November, Joe grabbed his jacket and sneaked out of the back door. He had arranged to meet Andy for an hour and he was a bit nervous because he knew his mum would disapprove. Still, she was in the lounge watching her favourite soap. Hopefully, Joe could be back in before she even noticed he was missing.

It was raining slightly and Joe pulled up the collar on his jacket as he headed for the Late Shop. That was where Andy and his friends hung out - on the corner by the Late Shop. They were already there. Joe heard them before he saw them. Andy was standing on a bench chanting a football song. His friends Abid and Kelly were bellowing with laughter.

'Well, look who it is!' shouted Andy as Joe approached. He had a plastic bag in his hand and he started swinging it above his head as he chanted his song again.

A shop assistant in a blue overall poked her head around the door and shouted at him.

'Will you kids keep the noise down! We can't hear ourselves think in here!'

'It's a free country!' Andy shouted back, and he pulled a face at her and carried on singing.

'If you don't shut up I'll send for the police!' retorted the shop assistant, and she disappeared back inside the store.

'I'll teach her a lesson,' snarled Andy, jumping down from the bench. 'Who does she think she is?'

22

'Go on, then,' encouraged Kelly.

'What are you going to do?' asked Abid.

Andy delved into the plastic bag he was holding and pulled out a firework. It was a banger with a picture of a red demon on the side. He produced a box of matches and lit the fuse. He held it at arm's length for a few seconds and then he threw it into the shop doorway. The explosion was almost instantaneous.

'Run!' shouted Andy, and the three teenagers raced from the scene, Joe chasing after them.

When they were a safe distance away, they stopped and burst into laughter. Joe didn't know what to do. He smiled feebly but he felt uncomfortable.

'Let's give that old bloke a fright,' suggested Andy, dipping into his plastic bag again. 'You know, the one who chased us off for hanging around outside his house. He only lives across the road. Come on.'

'You did throw your chip paper into his garden,' reminded Abid.

'And you broke his fence,' said Kelly. 'Still, he deserved it, didn't he?'

'What are you going to do?' asked Joe, as they approached a small terraced house. He knew who Andy was talking about. Joe's family had known Mr Smithson for years and his mum still visited him from time to time.

'You just watch,' sneered Andy. 'You might learn a few things if you watch me, Joe!'

Andy had hold of another firework. It was larger this time, with the words *Firecracker* printed on the side.

'I don't think you should,' stammered Joe, as Andy opened the gate and walked up the path.

'Don't be so soft!' snapped Andy, lighting the fuse. 'It'll be a right laugh! He'll jump out of his skin!'

The fuse fizzed into life and Andy shoved the firework through Mr Smithson's letter box. He turned and raced back up the path. There was a huge explosion just as Andy reached the gate.

'Wicked!' he shouted in excitement. 'Did you hear that one!'

But his friends did not respond. They were staring at the front door. Smoke was seeping from the bottom of the door and an orange glow could clearly be seen through the glass panel.

'What have you done!' gasped Abid. 'The place is on fire!'

The smile disappeared from Andy's face. In its place was a look of sheer panic.

'I'm out of here,' he said, and he turned and ran for all he was worth down the street, his friends chasing after him.

Joe was rooted to the spot. The orange glow had turned into deep red flames and smoke was pouring from the doorway. The fire was getting a hold. Joe glanced up as the curtains moved in the room directly above the door. It was Mr Smithson! He was there in the window and he would be trapped by the fire! Joe looked around in panic and then he dashed down the driveway of the house next door. Mr Smithson's neighbour was already on the front path.

'Call the Fire Brigade!' shouted Joe. 'We've got to get help! Mr Smithson's trapped inside!'

The engines arrived within minutes and the fire was soon under control. A shaken Mr Smithson, with a thick blanket draped over his shoulders, was led through the charred doorway to a waiting ambulance.

'It's just a precaution,' explained the neighbour, as a serious looking policeman walked across to join them. 'He'll be fine - thanks to your quick thinking! I dread to think what might have happened if you hadn't acted so quickly!'

Joe was shaking with fear. He took a deep breath, turned towards the policeman and said, 'Well . . . actually . . . there's something I need to tell you . . .'

Prayer: Lord, may we behave in a sensible and responsible manner at all times. May we never say or do anything that could cause harm to other people or to ourselves. Teach us to think for ourselves and not be easily led when we know that others are doing wrong. Amen.

Follow up: There are several points for discussion. Why was it dangerous for Joe to sneak out of the house without telling his parents? What do you think Joe should have done when he first saw Andy throwing a firework into the shop doorway? Where do you think Andy got the fireworks from? Does Joe deserve praise for his action in helping Mr Smithson or should he be in trouble for his part in the prank?

The story has implications in terms of peer pressure. Ask the children if they have ever felt pressured by friends to do something they knew to be wrong. Discuss ways of dealing with peer pressure.

A Foggy Day

Theme: The natural world/Weather

> **Introduction:** Most children will have experienced a foggy day. There will have been times through the year when they will have had to walk (or be driven!) to school on a foggy morning. This assembly draws on their own experience but it also informs about conditions years ago, especially when coal was the main fuel in most households and a foggy day meant arriving home covered in black smuts. Obviously, the assembly is best delivered if the weather is foggy.

It had been forecast the previous evening. The weather had been getting gradually colder and Rachel had woken up each morning to see the grass glistening with frost and a low mist hugging the ground.

'I don't mind the frost and a bit of mist,' said Rachel's dad, 'but I don't like fog. I hate driving in the fog – it can be really dangerous.'

The family were at the breakfast table, Rachel, her little brother Adam, mum and dad and Rachel's Gran, who was staying with them for a few days. They were staring out of the back window into a grey wall of thick fog. Rachel thought it felt strange. It was as if they were prisoners in their own home.

'We're lucky,' said Gran, sipping a hot mug of tea, 'we don't often get fog these days. You should have seen it when I was a girl!'

Rachel gave a sigh and pulled a face at Adam. Gran was always going on about when she was a girl!

'We used to get real fog,' continued Gran. 'Your Grandad used to call them 'pea soupers' because they were so thick. I can remember walking home from work and hardly being able to see an arm's length in front of me. People used to have accidents because they walked into lamp posts!'

Adam giggled and pretended to bang his head against a lamp post – but Gran didn't seem to notice. She just stared into the fog and continued her tale.

'I used to wrap a scarf right around my mouth because if you breathed in the fog you used to end up with a sore chest.'

'Why was that, Gran?' asked Rachel. She was beginning to get interested. 'Why did the fog give you a sore chest?'

'It was so dirty, you see,' explained Gran. 'When I was a young girl everyone had a coal fire.'

Rachel looked puzzled; she still did not understand.

'It was the smoke, Rachel. When it was foggy the smoke couldn't escape into the sky. It wasn't only the house chimneys, the factories used to pour out smoke as well. It used to mix with the fog and if you didn't cover your mouth you would breathe it in. You could smell it in the fog. I can remember arriving home after struggling through the fog and my face was black because of all the smoke in the fog.'

'It must have been horrible,' commented Adam. 'I'm glad we don't have smoky chimneys today.'

'Come on,' said mum, 'hurry up and finish your breakfast. We're going to be late for school!'

Ten minutes later they were ready to set off. Dad had already left for work. Rachel's mum had been worried about him driving and she watched him edge gingerly off the front drive and onto the road, the car head lamps doing their best to cut through the dense, still fog.

The two children were well wrapped up. It was so cold. Adam had the collar on his jacket pulled right up and he wore a scarf and a woollen hat which he pulled as far down over his forehead as he could. Rachel had the hood up on her coat but she was still freezing.

'Come on,' said mum, as Gran stood at the front door and watched them disappear into the fog, 'let's get you to school, should we?'

It wasn't far to school but it was a strange journey. Nowhere looked familiar. It was quiet too – eerily quiet. Cars moved slowly along the road, their headlights looming out of the fog like huge alien eyes; lamp posts appeared suddenly and voices seemed to be muffled and distant.

They arrived at the school gate and mum saw them safely into the playground. Even the school yard seemed different this foggy morning. No one was running around; the boys weren't playing football or chasing after the girls, annoying them as they usually did.

The bell for the start of the school day sounded early and Mrs Harris, the Deputy Headteacher called from the entrance for the children to make their way into school.

'Straight into your classes, please,' she instructed. 'It's too horrible to stay out here this morning!'

Rachel was glad to get inside. She had definitely decided that she didn't like the fog.

Later that morning, by playtime, the fog had almost disappeared. The sky was still hazy but thin rays of sun were forcing their way through. It was cold, it was crisp - but it was much better than the grey grasping fog.

Prayer: We know, Lord, that each and every day is different. When conditions are difficult, please keep us safe from harm. We think especially, this morning, of those who are most at risk from bad weather. We think of the elderly and the sick, of those who work out of doors and those who have to travel. We ask that you guard them and watch over them and keep them safe in your care. Amen.

Follow up: It is hard for children to imagine what it was like when smoke poured from house and factory chimneys. Most children are used to clean fuel and central

heating. Encourage them to talk to grandparents and to find out more about living conditions in the past.

Is society today less polluted? We may not have pollution from house and factory chimneys but there are far more cars on the road. Pollution from car fumes is particularly noticeable in summer when the weather is hot. Discuss what could be done to lessen such pollution.

A foggy day is an excellent stimulus for poetry. Discuss ideas together and then work in pairs to produce foggy day poems. Each new idea could begin with the words: *On a foggy day . . .*

e.g. *On a foggy day strange shapes loom towards you as you walk.*
   On a foggy day car head lamps pierce the gloom like alien eyes . . .

It's Photograph Day!

Theme: School photographs

Introduction: You should decide whether you wish to use this story before or after the visit of the school photographer! Begin by relating your own experiences of school photographs. If you are brave, you could bring in one of your old school photographs. Perhaps you have one of the long style photographs showing all the children in the school. Explain how lovely it is to keep a photographic record of your time at school. Parents and grandparents enjoy receiving the photographs but it is also good for you to look back at your time in school and remember your friends.

'Now, I'm sure you've all remembered - it's photograph day!' announced Mr Harker, closing the register and facing the class. 'Although why anyone would want a picture of some of you I'm not too sure!'

He giggled at his own joke as the children stared blankly.

'I hate photograph day,' complained Jordan Higgins. 'My photo never seems to turn out right.'

'That's because you always pull a face at the photographer,' explained Thomas Stephens, Jordan's best friend. 'What do you expect?'

'I want anyone with a younger brother or sister to go and collect them from their class,' continued Mr Harker. 'Make your way to the school hall. Mothers and babies should be there already.'

Jordan stood up and shuffled out of the classroom. His sister Amy was in the Reception Class and he had a younger brother who was just twelve months old. He collected Amy and then walked along the short corridor to the school hall. His mum was already there and Michael, his younger brother, spotted him immediately. He shouted out Jordan's name and waved his arms about wildly. Jordan looked embarrassed.

Mr Wilks, the school photographer, had set up against the back wall. A wooden bench was placed in front of a large screen which had a background that looked like a cloudy sky. Two huge spotlights focused on the middle of the bench. Mrs Harris, the Deputy Headteacher was busily organising children into a line so that the photographer could begin.

Jordan and his sister joined their mum and Thomas Stephens sat on the chair next to them.

'Where is Amanda Jane?' shouted an agitated Mrs Harris. 'Has anyone seen Amanda Jane?'

'She's in the washroom,' answered Lucy Jones, Amanda's friend. 'She's trying to make herself look beautiful, Mrs Harris!'

'That could take some time,' muttered Jordan. Amanda irritated him. She was a fussy girl with long, blonde curls.

The photographer tested his flashlight a few times and then he called the first group across to the bench. It was Lucy Jones, Amanda's friend. She sat on the middle of the bench, with her two little sisters, one on either side. Mr Wilks arranged them exactly as he wanted and then he moved back to his camera.

'A big smile . . . ' said Mr Wilks. 'Say sausages . . . '

'Soss-ig-is . . . ' chorused the three girls.

The light flashed twice and the girls moved away, giggling.

'I'm not saying sausages,' grumbled Jordan. 'It's stupid!'

'Stop complaining,' said his mum. 'We want a nice picture of you, don't we?'

Jordan scowled and watched as the next family group moved across to the bench and then his face brightened immediately. It was Edgar Brunt and his two brothers. They looked so funny. They sat there with their arms in front of them and three identical beams on their polished faces. But Edgar's hair was sticking up. He had tried to plaster it down with gel but one determined tuft on the top of his head had sprung up like a feather. The photographer walked over and patted it down with his hand. He smiled in satisfaction, returned to the camera - and the offending tuft sprung up stiffly again.

'It'll be fine!' lied the photographer. 'Three big smiles, please! Say sausages . . .'

Flash! The photograph was taken - tuft and all!

Eventually, it was Jordan's turn. Little Michael was crying by now and Amy was desperately trying to cheer him up. They sat on the bench and Michael howled. Mr Wilks waved a battered old teddy in front of him which seemed to make him howl louder. After a few moments he grabbed the teddy and started chewing its ear. At least that quietened him. Mr Wilks rushed back to his camera and prepared for the photograph.

'Three big smiles, please! Say sausages . . .'

Jordan forced a smile but just as the camera flashed Michael swung the teddy and hit him in the face!

'Oh, dear! I think we'll try that again!' said Mr Wilks. 'Big smiles everyone . . .'

The camera flashed and to Jordan's relief they were allowed to leave the bench.

'That should be lovely!' crooned Jordan's mum. 'Your nose might be a bit red where Michael hit you with the teddy but I'm sure it will make a lovely photograph!'

'At least it's over for another year,' thought Jordan as Amanda Jane beamed from beneath her blonde curls on the photographer's bench.

'Where is Belinda Humphries!' shouted a demented Mrs Harris. 'Has anyone seen Belinda Humphries?'

Prayer: Dear Lord, we know that memories are precious. Help us to treasure our memories. It is wonderful to keep a record of ourselves and our brothers and sisters growing up. May we look back upon our happy time at school with fondness and may our school photographs help to preserve our lovely memories. Amen.

29

Follow up: Encourage the children to ask their parents and grandparents if they still have photographs from their school days. See if they can bring a photograph into school together with some information as to when and where it was taken. Ask the children to find out how life at school was different for their parents and grandparents.

Ask the children to bring in their favourite photograph. The photographs can be discussed in class and the children could write about the content of the photo and give an explanation as to why they have chosen it.

Ask the children to bring in a photograph of themselves as a baby. Number each photograph and make a gallery. They will love trying to work out exactly who is who!

Barry's Bad Lunchtime

Theme: Dinnertime behaviour

Introduction: In many schools, dinnertime provides a flashpoint for behavioural difficulties. This assembly can be used as either a reminder or a warning as to how the children should behave at dinnertime. It also reminds the children to show respect to the lunchtime supervisors.

Begin by asking the children what the word respect means. The Oxford dictionary defines respect using words such as regard, attention, consideration and politeness. Remind the children that when they are in school you expect them to show respect both to members of staff and to other children. Politeness, good manners and good behaviour should become a habit for everyone.

Barry liked school. He always worked hard and he seldom got into trouble. His parents had brought him up to be a polite, considerate boy and this was reflected in the way that he went about his daily routines. He was popular with the other children and well liked by the school staff. If a teacher wanted a job done, Barry was often chosen because he was so sensible and reliable. It came as a great surprise to everyone, therefore, when Barry began to get into trouble.

It all started when a new boy joined the school. Kevin Cropper was placed on the same table as Barry in class and it soon became obvious to Mrs Gale, the teacher, and to the other children that Kevin Cropper was a nuisance. He seemed more interested in chatting than getting on with his work and he was always messing around, flicking rubbers or drawing on his books. It was only his second morning in school when he snapped Emily Parker's ruler and blamed it on the girl sitting next to him! Mrs Gale was well aware of what had happened and Kevin missed his morning playtime.

For some strange reason, Barry found Kevin Cropper funny. He laughed at his silly jokes and he was amused when Kevin did something naughty. He even found it funny when Kevin deliberately knocked a pot of dirty paint water over everyone's work. Mrs Gale was surprised at Barry and she kept him behind at the end of the school day to have a quiet word with him.

'If I were you, I'd choose my friends very carefully,' warned Mrs Gale. 'There's one particular boy in this class who will get you into trouble!'

Barry took no notice. He and Kevin became more and more friendly and Barry's behaviour started to deteriorate.

One lunchtime, Kevin and Barry got into real trouble. Kevin had been messing around in the dining hall, playing with his food and deliberately annoying the other

children around him. Barry had started to join in and Mrs Hill, one of the lunchtime supervisors told the boys more than once to behave. It was only when Kevin pulled a face behind Mrs Hill's back and Emily told over him that the two boys were made to stand against the wall in the school hall - but even then they wouldn't stop giggling.

Their behaviour did not improve once they were outside in the school yard. They disrupted the football game and tormented the girls.

'Will you leave the other children alone!' shouted Mrs Hill, in frustration. 'If you can't play with them nicely just leave them alone!'

'Why should we,' muttered Kevin under his breath. 'It's good fun annoying them!'

Emily Parker was skipping with her friends when her shoe came off. Quick as a flash, Kevin scooped it from the floor and threw it to Barry.

'Give it back!' demanded Emily, hopping on one foot.

'Why should we!' retorted Barry, and he threw it back to Kevin who ran off with it across the yard.

'Mrs Hill!' shouted Emily. 'Kevin Cropper's ran off with my shoe!'

Mrs Hill shouted after Kevin at once - but he ignored her. He showed her no respect whatsoever. In fact, he ran towards her and then tossed the shoe over her head to Barry, laughing out loud as he did so.

'Throw it back!' he screamed. 'Throw it back, Barry!'

Barry hurled the shoe back towards his friend, so hard that it flew past Kevin - straight towards the staffroom window. Barry froze in panic as the shoe smashed into the window, showering glass everywhere. There were angry shouts from inside the staffroom and Mr Burgess, the Headteacher appeared at the door, his face red with rage.

'Who is responsible?' he bellowed, as the children in the yard became suddenly silent.

Kevin Cropper raised his finger and pointed at Barry.

'It was him, Sir,' he whined, accusingly. 'Barry hurled Emily's shoe through the window, Sir!'

Barry couldn't believe it! He thought Kevin was his friend.

'Go and stand outside my room, please, Barry,' ordered the angry Headteacher. 'You've got a bit of explaining to do!'

Barry walked forlornly towards the school entrance. The words of Mrs Gale, his class teacher, were ringing in his ears:

'If I were you, I would choose my friends very carefully, Barry.'

Prayer: Dear Lord, teach us to be polite and considerate at all times. May we always show respect to those who are older and wiser and may we learn to behave in a sensible and responsible manner. When we are tempted to be led astray, help us to stop and think and choose the right path, safe in the knowledge that you are watching over us. Amen.

Follow up: The story focuses on lunchtime behaviour but it is also about choosing friends carefully. Why do you think a previously sensible boy such as Barry became friendly with Kevin Cropper?

What do you think happened next in the story? Does Kevin get away with his awful behaviour or does Mrs Hill, the lunchtime supervisor intervene. Write the next part of the story. Perhaps you could make it clear that Barry has learnt his lesson.

Every Dog has its Day

Theme: Caring for pets

Introduction: Begin by asking the children generally about their pets. Ask a few of the children what their pets are called, how they look after them etc. Choose somebody who has a dog. Pretend that you would like a dog and ask the child if he/she would give you his/her pet. When the child declines, ask why he/she would not give the dog away? Of course, you should praise the child for being so caring and explain that once you take ownership of a pet you have a duty to love and care for it. Unfortunately, as in today's story, not everyone feels the same way.

The Cragg family lived in a very comfortable semi-detached house not far out of the town centre. There was Mr Cragg, who worked as a clerk in the Local Government offices, Mrs Cragg, who worked part-time in the nearby superstore, and their two teenage children, Simon and Donna. Oh, and there was one more member of the Cragg family - an old, brown spaniel called Buster, who, when he was not asleep in his basket, spent most of his time in the cramped back garden.

The Craggs had owned Buster since he was a puppy. Of course, when they first got him Donna and Simon were young children and they were delighted to have a playful puppy. Mrs Cragg didn't really want a dog but she gave in to the children just to keep them quiet. Mr Cragg just did as he was told! And Buster was playful - sometimes a little bit too playful! There was the time, for example, when he ripped Mrs Cragg's new cushions to bits. He took each one in his mouth in turn and shook it until the stuffing flew out. Mrs Cragg was so angry she threw him out into the back garden and wouldn't let him back into the house for two days. It was a sign of things to come.

The chicken wasn't Buster's fault, either. Buster had taken it off the kitchen table thinking it had been left there for him. He wasn't to know Mrs Cragg was letting it cool down so that she could carve it more easily. That incident led to another two days in the garden. It had been freezing cold and Buster was given no food. Still, the family were all right with him most of the time. Besides, he knew no different.

The problem was that as Donna and Simon grew older, they completely lost interest in Buster. Donna took up dancing lessons; she played rounders in summer and hockey in winter. When she was at home she disappeared up into her bedroom to listen to her music. She had no time for Buster. Simon was just as busy. He was football mad. He trained twice a week and played for his local team every Saturday morning. When he wasn't playing football he spent his time playing computer games. He couldn't be bothered to take Buster for a walk. Mrs Cragg began to get more and more angry with Buster. He always seemed to be there,

34

getting under her feet in the kitchen, jumping onto the furniture in the lounge, lying at the top of the stairs where she would fall over him. Consequently, he was thrown out into the back garden more and more.

Mr Cragg didn't protest; he did as he was told.

For Mrs Cragg, the final straw came one wet Friday in February. She had just arrived home from work and she was soaking. It had been pouring with rain and she had missed the 4 o'clock bus. She was sitting at the kitchen table having a cup of hot, steaming tea when the back door opened and Simon sauntered in. Poor Buster, who had been left out in the garden as usual, took his chance. He darted into the kitchen and shook himself violently. Mrs Cragg let out a scream as she was showered with water. Buster knew at once that he was in trouble. He ran into the lounge and jumped onto the sofa, his muddy paws leaving brown trails across the beige cushions.

'Get him off!' screamed Mrs Cragg. She was standing in the doorway flapping her arms.

Buster leapt off the couch and ran up the stairs, Simon and his mother chasing after him. Buster was scared. He jumped up onto Mrs Cragg's double bed, left a trail of dirty marks and then dashed back out onto the landing. Mrs Cragg was there, at the top of the stairs, and Buster took his chance. He darted straight between her legs, flew back downstairs and raced back out into the security of the garden.

'That's it!' said Mrs Cragg, as she sat down on the top of the stairs and clasped her hand to her forehead. 'That dog's got to go! I've just about had enough of him!'

Simon shrugged his shoulders and disappeared to play on his computer. He didn't care about Buster anymore. When Donna heard the news, she too, seemed totally unconcerned. Mr Cragg didn't say a word - he just did as he was told.

The following day, Mrs Cragg found Buster's lead (which hadn't been used for years) and, together with Simon, they left the house with an excited Buster trailing behind. Buster had no idea that he was going to be taken somewhere and abandoned.

'We'll let him loose in the park at the edge of town,' said Mrs Cragg, coldly. 'Once he's run off we can slip away and leave him.'

Simon didn't answer. He was listening to some music on his personal CD player.

They had just reached the end of the street when Mr Moss came around the corner. He was an elderly man who lived alone a few doors away from the Cragg family.

'Hello,' he said, looking surprised, 'I haven't seen you walking with Buster for some time! I didn't know you still had him!'

Buster wagged his tail and whimpered with excitement.

'We won't have him for much longer,' snapped Mrs Cragg, anxious to get on with the job. 'He's nothing but a nuisance! He's got to go!'

'Got to go?' repeated Mr Moss, suspiciously. 'What do you mean he's got to go?'

'I mean,' said Mrs Cragg, slowly and deliberately, 'he's not coming back in my house! We're going to get rid of him.'

'But there's nothing wrong with him,' protested Mr Moss. 'He's a perfectly healthy dog. What are you going to do with him?'

'I think that's our business!' snapped Mrs Cragg, impatiently, and she started to walk off.

'Wait a minute,' said Mr Moss, grabbing her arm. 'I live all on my own. If you're really going to get rid of him I'd love to give him a home. Would you let me buy him from you?'

'You mean you'd pay money for him?' said Mrs Cragg. She was suddenly interested. 'How much would you give me?'

'Would ten pounds be all right?' asked Mr Moss. He begrudged giving the woman a penny but he was determined to save Buster.

'Ten pounds would be very acceptable,' replied Mrs Cragg, her eyes lighting up with greed.

'It's a deal then,' said Mr Moss, and he handed over a ten pound note and accepted the lead from Mrs Cragg.

Buster looked puzzled as the old man led him away - but he still wagged his tail wildly. He wasn't afraid of this kind, old man. His animal instinct told him that life was going to be much, much better from now on.

Prayer: Lord, we know that keeping a pet is a tremendous responsibility. Animals have feelings just as humans do. May we always look after our pets and treat them kindly. May we never do anything that could harm or frighten them and may we learn to love and appreciate our pets as true friends. Amen.

Follow up: The children could conduct a 'pet survey' in class to find out which is the most popular animal kept as a pet. The data could be interpreted in different forms of graphs.

The children could bring in pictures of their pets and even write a brief 'pet biography', including any funny incidents. The writing and pictures would make an effective display.

Look for any poems about pets or animals. These can be read out in class and the children can have a go at writing their own 'pet poems'.

Cat in the Cold

Theme: Caring for pets

> **Introduction:** This is a good story to use when there is a spell of cold weather. Begin by asking the children: 'Who has a pet at home?' This can lead to a discussion about different types of pets, names, caring for pets etc. Ask all the children who own cats to raise their hands. Enquire as to whether any of the cats have funny names! Explain that although cats often like to go out at night, when the weather is really cold it is much kinder to keep them indoors.
>
> The people who owned the cat in today's story were so uncaring that the cat decided he was better off outside in the freezing cold.

Oscar crawled beneath the garden shed, curled up into a tight ball - and shivered. It was a freezing cold February night. Earlier that day it had snowed, leaving the ground covered with a thin blanket of white. Oscar hated the snow and he tried to get back into the house. The two children had been trying to build a snowman in the garden but as soon as they saw Oscar they thought of a much better game.

'Let's see if we can hit him with a snowball!' yelled Wayne, shaping a handful of soft snow.

'I bet my aim's better than yours!' shouted Chantelle, and she flung the first missile towards the unsuspecting cat.

Oscar didn't wait to find out who had the better shot, he turned tail and jumped over the garden fence as a volley of snowballs followed him.

'Dumb cat!' laughed Wayne. 'We'll get him when he comes back!'

Oscar had no intention of coming back. He had had enough of the dreadful Wayne and Chantelle - and of their equally dreadful parents. He was fed up of having various objects thrown at him, being tossed off the chairs, getting drenched with cups of water. To make matters worse, he was hungry. Oscar was never fed properly. His filthy dish received occasional scraps of disgusting leftovers that weren't even fit for a rat - let alone a cat! He had made up his mind - he was going to look for a home elsewhere.

And so there he was, huddled beneath the garden shed. As soon as darkness fell, the sky had cleared and the temperature had dropped to well below freezing. Of course, Oscar was used to spending cold nights outside. After all, he was thrown out to fend for himself every night - but this particular February night was especially cold and Oscar had not eaten for days. He was feeling completely miserable.

After a couple of hours, Oscar decided to take a walk. There was a shop nearby that often threw away scraps of food. If the bins were full they sometimes spilled over and Oscar could help himself to some supper. The cautious cat approached the yard with care. The shopkeeper didn't like him and he didn't want a drenching on this cold night. He squeezed beneath the yard gate and stared in disappointment at the great metal bins. They were firmly fastened and covered with frost. Feeling disappointed and disheartened, Oscar left the yard to look for comfort elsewhere.

He wandered through the back streets for more than an hour. Oscar had never been so far before and although he was confident that he could find his way home, he had no intention of doing so. He reached a row of terraced houses and decided to investigate the back yards. The first yard was a disaster! A huge ginger Tom cat hissed and spat at him so that Oscar turned tail and fled in fear. He missed out the next few houses and tried again further along the row. It was much more promising. He entered a yard that was flooded with a welcoming yellow light. The light seemed to come from a kitchen area and it was accompanied by a delicious smell. The family had obviously had roast chicken for their dinner and the chicken smell drifted from an open kitchen window.

Oscar stared at the dustbin and realised that if he leapt on top of it he would just about be able to jump through the open window. It was risky but he was so hungry that he decided to give it a go. The first part was easy but once on top of the bin his leap to the window looked much more daunting. He would have to get it absolutely right or he would smack against the window and land on the cold floor. He crouched low and concentrated. He flexed his legs - and leapt. Oscar's claws clutched at the wooden surround and, for a moment, he dangled precariously. Summoning the little strength he had left, he hauled himself through the small gap and jumped down onto the kitchen work surface.

What luck! There was a plate of left over chicken right in front of his nose! Oscar couldn't resist it! He tucked in immediately, the succulent chicken tasting better than anything he had ever tasted before. Two minutes later the plate was clean and Oscar couldn't help but purr loudly. He liked this house. It felt good and he decided to investigate further.

Passing through the open kitchen door, he found himself in a small hallway. A set of stairs led to the upper floor and Oscar felt strangely drawn to climb them. At the top of the stairs, he could see an open door and he couldn't believe his luck - there was a bed! Checking for humans and sensing none around, he leapt onto the soft bed and settled down in the corner nearest to the wall. It was heaven. He washed his paws for a couple of minutes before curling up into a tight ball and drifting into a wonderful, dream filled sleep.

Oscar was awakened by a squeal. His head jerked upwards and his eyes opened to see a little girl standing beside the bed. She was clutching a battered teddy bear and she had a look of delightful astonishment on her face.

'Mummy - it's a cat! A real live cat! And it's been fast asleep on my bed!'

A tall lady appeared through the open doorway, a frown on her face. 'That explains where the chicken went, Alice! And to think - I blamed your father!'

'What's it doing on my bed?' asked Alice, moving forward and scratching Oscar's head.

Oscar purred loudly and tried to look appealing.

'Don't touch it,' ordered mum. 'It might have fleas, Alice!'

Oscar felt offended. Fleas, indeed. Actually, he did have a few - but it wasn't his fault.

'Can we keep it?' pleaded Alice. 'I've always wanted a cat and this one has chosen us, hasn't it?'

'Well, I don't know about that,' replied mum, 'but it does look as if it needs a bit of love and attention - and we certainly can't throw it back out in the cold tonight. I'll have a word with your father and we'll see what we can do.'

'Oh, thanks mum,' said an excited Alice. 'My very own cat! I think I'll call it Tiddles!'

Oscar looked alarmed but he stayed calm.

'There's an old basket in the garage,' said mum. 'I'll line it with a nice blanket and Tiddles can sleep in the kitchen for the night.'

Oscar could not believe his luck! His very own basket; a nice blanket; sleep in the kitchen. He might be called Tiddles from now on but no longer would he be a cat in the cold!

Prayer: Dear Lord, we share this planet with many other living creatures. May we learn to respect the animals, birds and insects. We especially think of our pets this morning, who rely on us for love, care and attention. May we never betray their trust. Amen.

Follow up: Those children who have pets might like to write about their animals, concentrating on the care they provide. Ask them to include any humorous incidents involving their pets. Some of the children could present their work in a subsequent assembly.

Ask the children if they can find any poems about animals. These could also be read out in assembly.

Twin Trouble

Theme: The value of hard work, responsibility and good organisation

Introduction: Begin by telling the children that you have to be very well organised in the morning. Explain that it is important to have your bag packed ready for school and that you need to make sure that you do not forget anything. It is important that you have your assembly planned. It would be awful if you were standing at the front of the hall and you did not know what to say! Tell the children that you keep a diary so that you are organised for the days and weeks ahead. You could read out one or two of the events you have in your diary. Explain that you feel happier and work better if you are well organised.

Tell the children that as they grow older and work their way through school they gradually learn to take more responsibility for their own lives. If they don't learn to become responsible people then all sorts of things could go wrong - as shown by one of the characters in today's story.

James and Harry Fisher were twins. They looked exactly the same and even people who knew them well had great difficulty telling them apart. You would have to stare very closely into each of their faces to notice that Harry had slightly more freckles than his brother, particularly around his nose. However, I'm sure you realise that it is very rude to stare!

Although they looked the same, their personalities were very different. James was the first awake and the first out of bed every morning, usually leaving his brother fast asleep and snoring on the bottom bunk. He was first to the bathroom and he was first down to breakfast. The toast was usually stone cold by the time Harry arrived at the table.

'I don't care,' Harry would say, yawning. 'I like cold toast!'

James would have his bag ready packed for school while Harry hunted high and low for his missing pencil case or lost P.E. kit. Furthermore, Harry regularly got into trouble with Mrs Browning, his class teacher, for not returning his homework. There were several occasions when he had just forgotten to bring it back to school but there were many more times when he had not taken it home in the first place.

You have probably got the message by now that Harry was completely disorganised. He had no sense of responsibility whatsoever.

Harry's parents despaired of him. They couldn't understand what had gone wrong. Both boys had been treated in exactly the same way and yet they were so different.

Mr and Mrs Fisher had booked a short break at a family hotel in The Lake District for Half Term. They felt sure it would please everyone. The boys would be able to

take part in some adventure activities and they themselves could enjoy the beautiful scenery. The night before they were due to go the boys were asked to pack their bags. James did not have a problem but Harry's attempt at packing was a disaster. He had left his training shoes and his track suit at school and he couldn't find his waterproof jacket. After searching the bedroom for half an hour, he eventually found two pairs of denims underneath his bunk bed. One pair was ripped and the other pair was so damp and dirty that green mould had started to form.

'I thought there was a funny smell in here,' said Harry, looking puzzled. He tossed the disgusting denims into the wash bag and turned towards his brother. 'Have you got a spare pair of jeans to lend me?' he asked, hopefully.

'Sorry,' replied James. 'I've only got one decent pair and I've already packed them.'

Harry threw a pair of shorts into his bag and hoped that the weather would be warm. He peered under his bed again and pulled out his toothbrush. It was very grubby and covered with fluff.

'I wondered where that had got to,' commented Harry, and he tossed it into his bag on top of the shorts.

'When was the last time you cleaned your teeth?' asked James, shaking his head in disbelief. 'You won't have any teeth to clean in a few years time!'

'That will be one job less to do then, won't it?' said Harry, and he stuck his head back beneath the bunk to see what else he could find.

Unfortunately, it rained non stop during their time in The Lake District. It didn't bother James or his parents but Harry was freezing cold and hardly left the hotel. Of course, his parents could have bought him some warmer clothes while they were there but it seemed the perfect opportunity to teach Harry a lesson.

It did seem to work. Harry made a determined effort to get himself better organised. James was still first up each morning but Harry stumbled out of bed soon afterwards. James was first to the bathroom but Harry followed a few minutes later. His parents had treated him to a new toothbrush which he actually remembered to use. He had started to pack his school bag each evening which meant that he was better organised for the start of the school day. He even remembered to complete his homework and hand it in at school - well, on most occasions.

The strange thing was that Harry felt much better about himself and the more organised he became the happier he felt about life. Of course, it caused a huge problem for all those who knew the twins. They were now alike in personality as well as in looks. It was no wonder that people started staring at them more intensely to see which one had the most freckles!

Prayer: Teach us, Lord, to take responsibility for our own actions. Help us to be well organised, dependable and reliable. May we grow up to be sensible and caring people who always consider the needs of others. Amen.

41

Follow up: There may be times when acting in a responsible way takes a great deal of courage. It is not always easy to say 'no' when friends are tempting you to do wrong. Ask the children if they can think of any examples.

Most jobs carry a great deal of responsibility. Discuss the responsibilities of different roles, such as a nurse, a policeman, a teacher, a politician, a road sweeper. Show that all roles are important and that everyone has a part to play if we are to have a successful, well ordered society.

Discuss different types of irresponsible behaviour in society (such as graffiti, bullying, crime etc.). What are the effects of such behaviour? Do the children have any ideas as to how such behaviour can be controlled?

The Grumpy Giant

Theme: Everyone feels better for a smile

> **Introduction:** Begin by asking the children if they have ever felt really grumpy. Ask them what sort of things make them grumpy. Listen to some answers. You might want to tell the children about something that makes you grumpy - e.g. children who do not listen or who misbehave in assembly! Explain that it is far better to be cheerful and much nicer to see a smiling face than one that is always frowning. Tell the children that today's story should give them something to smile about.

'It's not fair!' growled Gregor the Giant, as he curled up on the cold, hard rocks at the back of his deep coastal cave. 'It's freezing in here and it's damp as well. Why can't I have a nice, dry sandy cave like my cousin George? Life's not fair!'

Outside, the wind howled and the waves crashed over the rocks and into the mouth of the cave.

'And I'm not lighting a fire again,' grumbled Gregor. He had a habit of talking to himself. He was so grumpy that no one else would listen to him. 'All that smoke filling the cave and making me cough. Besides, last time I tried to light a fire I burnt my fingers. Fires are stupid. I don't see why they have to be so hot!'

A flash of lightning lit up the cave's entrance and Gregor grimaced and ground his teeth.

'A storm,' he grunted. 'That's just great. It will probably keep me awake all night. In fact, there's no point in trying to sleep. I'll just sit here and shiver all night long.'

And he did. He sat and grumbled and complained to himself all night long, well after the storm had passed over and the wind had calmed down, leaving only gentle waves lapping into the mouth of the cave.

Just as the morning sun was breaking, Gregor's eyes became heavy and he drifted into an uneasy sleep.

Outside, on the shingle beach, two young children were up early collecting shells, enjoying the morning sunshine. Brendan and Jessica were on holiday and their parents could see them from the end of their cottage garden near the top of the cliffs.

'Don't go too far!' shouted dad, leaning over the gate. 'Breakfast will be ready in five minutes!'

'We won't,' promised Brendan, giving his dad a friendly wave. 'And we'll keep together.'

It was then that Jessica noticed the cave. Strange - they had walked along the beach the previous day and had never noticed the gaping entrance.

'Let's go and explore,' she said, excitedly. 'I bet there are lots of shells in the cave entrance.'

'I'm not sure we should,' replied her brother, cautiously. 'Dad won't be able to see us if we disappear into a cave.'

'Don't be so soft,' said Jessica, scrambling over the rocks towards the dark opening. 'Besides, we don't need to go right in - we can just take a look.'

'Just a look then,' agreed Brendan, following his sister, 'and then we'll go home for some breakfast, eh?'

A few moments later the two children crept across the soft sand at the entrance to the giant's cave. Brendan heard it first and he grabbed hold of his sister's arm. Yes, he could hear it - a steady, low grunting noise followed by a long sigh. It sounded strangely familiar - a little like his dad when he fell asleep in the chair - but it was louder and stronger.

'I don't like it!' he whimpered, backing away from the gaping entrance. 'There's something horrible in the cave, Jessica! I don't like it!'

'Somebody might have been trapped by the storm,' suggested Jessica. 'Someone could be hurt. We should see if we can help.' And she moved further into the cave, leaving her brother to edge in after her.

It was dark and it was musty and even Jessica felt a little scared. Suddenly, Gregor gave a great snort in his sleep and Jessica jumped as she saw the huge figure slumped towards the back of the vast cave. Brendan saw him, too. He opened his mouth to scream but he was so scared that no sound came out.

Sensing that someone was in his cave, Gregor opened his eyes slowly and stared around. He spotted the two tiny children, his eyes opened wider and he grunted in annoyance.

'Who are you?' he grumbled. 'And what are you doing here? No one ever visits me!'

'We're on holiday,' stammered Jessica, staring at the giant in disbelief. 'We saw the cave entrance and . . . We didn't mean to disturb you.'

'No one ever visits me,' repeated the giant. 'That's why I'm so grumpy.' He sat up and folded his arms and scowled.

'Yes, you are a bit grumpy, aren't you?' agreed Jessica. 'But I'm not sure why. You live in a nice dry cave by the seaside and there must be lots of people on the beach who you can talk to.'

'Nobody would want to talk to me,' complained Gregor. 'I'm too grumpy.'

'Perhaps if you tried,' suggested Brendan, growing in confidence. 'Perhaps if you were to try a little smile?'

'A little smile?' repeated the giant. 'I don't think I know how to smile.'

Brendan and Jessica exchanged glances. 'Watch us,' said Jessica and the two children stepped forward and gave him a big grin.

'You see, it's easy!' Jessica assured him. 'Go on, now it's your turn!'

'Oh, I don't know . . .' simpered the giant. 'What if I don't like it?'

'Go on,' insisted Jessica. 'You'll love it. I know you will. It will make you feel better.'

'Oh, all right then,' agreed Gregor. 'If you're absolutely sure. . .'

He licked his lips, he blinked his eyes, he took a deep breath and ever so

44

slowly, his face creased into a spreading smile.

'Wonderful!' cheered Jessica.

'Splendid!' agreed Brendan. 'It makes you look really handsome!'

'Do you think so?' enthused the giant, the smile still fixed on his face. 'Do you really think so?'

'We do!' agreed the children, and they nodded their heads up and down and beamed back at him.

'I think I'll keep it,' said Gregor, grinning broadly. 'Now that I've found it, I think I'll keep it!'

'You see,' said Jessica, 'there's no need to feel grumpy, is there? Everyone feels better if they just remember to smile!'

Prayer: Lord, help us to be positive and always look on the bright side of life. We have so much for which to be thankful in this world. Help us to appreciate the many wonderful gifts that you have provided and may we remember that life is so much better when each new day is approached with a smile. Amen.

Follow up: The children could be encouraged to write poems entitled 'What Makes Me Smile.' They could start with a list which can be expanded using adjectives, adverbs etc.

e.g. The clear, blue morning sky always makes me smile.

The warm, lapping waves when I am on holiday at the seaside always make me smile.

Theme: Honesty

> **Introduction:** It is sometimes difficult to tell the truth, especially if you know you are going to get into trouble as a result. However, if you get into the habit of telling lies eventually you will get into even more trouble. People who constantly tell lies may get away with it for a while but in the end they are always caught out.
>
> The young girl in this story was eventually caught out by her conscience.

Lucy didn't mean to lie, she just found it difficult to tell the truth. It all started when she was quite young. In fact, she was just four years old when she crept upstairs and took her mum's lipstick out of the make-up bag. She could hardly see her own face in the mirror she was that small. She did manage to smudge a bit around her mouth but she decided that she would really have to practise on someone else. She thought about her dolls at first but then she had a much better idea. Her little brother Daniel was strapped into his high chair in the kitchen. Mum was on the phone. It was perfect. Lucy chose two contrasting shades - bright pink and dark red - and then she got to work. She drew two pink circles around his eyes, at first and then she coloured his nose dark red. Daniel sat there as good as gold and giggled. He was beginning to look like a reindeer. Lucy had just started on his cheeks when she heard mum say 'goodbye' on the phone. She dropped the lipsticks onto Daniel's tray, rushed across to the kitchen table and pretended to be looking at a comic. Mum stopped in her tracks when she entered the kitchen.

'Daniel! What on earth has happened to you!'

Daniel gurgled again and began to eat one of the lipsticks. Lucy's mum rushed across and grabbed it off him, quickly - and then she turned to face Lucy.

'How could you!' she stormed. 'He could have been really sick if he'd eaten that lipstick!'

'It wasn't me!' lied Lucy. 'I don't know where he got them from!'

Lucy's mum shook her head and went to get some wipes to clean Daniel.

A few months later Lucy was staying at her Grandma's house. She loved staying with Grandma. She always got her own way. It was early evening and Lucy was sitting on the sofa watching television. She was fiddling with a table lamp which was on a stand at the side of the sofa. Grandma's cat, Tiddles, was fast asleep on the chair nearby.

'Lucy, don't fiddle with the lamp, please,' said Grandma, getting up to make a cup of tea. 'I've had it a long time and I don't want it broken.'

'All right, Grandma,' said Lucy, but she kept switching it on and off as Grandma left the room.

The next moment there was a crash as the china lamp toppled to the floor. Tiddles leapt in the air. Her fur stood out stiff like a frightened hairbrush.

'Lucy - what did I tell you!' groaned Grandma, reappearing at the door. 'Now look what you've done!'

'It wasn't me!' lied Lucy. 'It was Tiddles! She jumped up and caught the wire. That's why she looks so frightened.'

Grandma shook her head in dismay as Tiddles stared wide-eyed at the smashed lamp.

The lying continued when Lucy started school. Lucy's class was preparing for the Christmas Nativity Play and, secretly, Lucy was a little bit jealous that she had not been chosen as an angel. It was all right being a sheep but her best friend Beth was an angel. Mrs Hargreaves had hung up the costumes carefully in the corner of the classroom and warned the children to keep away from them. Of course, Lucy couldn't resist it! While Mrs Hargreaves was hearing some children read, Lucy crept into the corner and took Beth's angel costume from its hanger. She was just putting it over her head when Mrs Hargreaves called her out to read. Lucy panicked. She pulled at the costume and there was a loud ripping sound. The classroom fell silent as Mrs Hargreaves made her way from her desk towards Lucy.

Lucy thought quickly. 'Somebody must have been playing with it, Mrs Hargreaves. I was just putting it back on the hanger for you but it seems to have caught on something.'

Mrs Hargreaves put her hands on her hips and stared hard at Lucy, who had an innocent face - just like an angel.

It was a whole year later that Lucy's lying really got her into trouble. They were in a new class and Mrs Mace had asked a couple of the children to stay in at lunchtime and mix some paint for the afternoon lesson. Lucy could not understand why her friend Beth was always chosen to do the jobs. She didn't realise it was because Beth was so reliable. After she had finished her dinner, Lucy sneaked back into the classroom.

'Lucy!' said Beth, adding some water to a pot of blue paint. 'You shouldn't be here. You'll get into trouble!'

'Who's going to know about it?' replied Lucy, skipping across the room. 'You won't tell anyone, will you?'

'I suppose not,' said Beth, but she looked uncomfortable. 'Mind you don't knock the paint pots over. I've just filled them up.'

She had no sooner spoken than Lucy caught her foot on a chair leg and stumbled forward. She lurched into the table sending the paint pots scattering everywhere. What a mess! Paint spilled across the art paper and spattered over the library books. It was everywhere!

'Lucy!' gasped Beth. 'Look what you've done!'

'It wasn't me!' stammered Lucy, instinctively, and she picked herself up and ran out of the classroom.

Ten minutes later, when the bell had sounded for afternoon lessons, Lucy crept back into class, sheepishly. Mrs Mace looked furious. Beth was standing in front of the teacher's desk and Mrs Mace was wagging her finger at her. Lucy felt awful. Her stomach was churning. She had never experienced such a dreadful feeling in her life.

And then she knew what she had to do. She approached the teacher's desk and said in a quivering voice: 'I'm sorry, Mrs Mace but it wasn't Beth - it was me! I crept back into the classroom and I stumbled into the paint pots. I'm really sorry, Mrs Mace.'

There was a moment's pause and then Lucy burst into tears.

Prayer: Sometimes, Lord, we are tempted to tell lies even when we know that this is unacceptable. Give us the courage to own up if we have done something wrong. Teach us the habit of telling the truth. May we learn that honesty is the best policy and may we live our lives by following your example. Amen.

Follow up: Discuss the concept of conscience. Ask the children if they have ever done something that they knew to be wrong and then felt guilty about their actions. Explain that conscience often acts as a control and stops you from doing something that you know to be wrong.

Plan a short story together in which conscience acts as a control. You should think about your characters, the setting and the plot. The children could then work either individually or in pairs to write their own versions of the story.

Leroy's Lies

Theme: Honesty

> **Introduction:** Sometimes there is a thin line between telling a lie and over exaggerating. For example, if you have been playing in a football or rounders match, you might go home and boast about how fantastic you were when, in truth, you just did O.K. There might not be any harm in what you say but you should be careful that your exaggerations don't turn into more serious lies. If you get into the habit of telling lies they will definitely lead you into trouble.

Leroy had convinced himself that he didn't tell lies - he just had a fantastic imagination. From the very first day he had started school, Mrs Fisher, his class teacher, had been suspicious, but she had listened to Leroy's tales with amusement.

'My daddy is a detective,' Leroy explained, proudly. 'He drives a fast car and solves difficult cases.'

'Does he really,' said Mrs Fisher, suppressing a smile. She knew full well that Leroy's dad worked in the local biscuit factory. 'I expect he's just undercover at the moment, is he?'

Leroy didn't really understand but he nodded vigorously.

Then there was the time in Year 2 when Leroy's class went on a school trip to Chester Zoo. Leroy hadn't stopped talking all the way round the zoo and when they arrived at the lion's enclosure Leroy announced: 'My dad went on safari to Africa last week. He was cornered by a lion but he fought his way out.'

'Did he really?' said Leroy's teacher, and turning away she muttered, 'What a pity he didn't take you with him!'

Leroy's lies were harmless enough but the older he grew the more he got into the habit of lying. Furthermore, his classmates had got that used to his tales that Leroy progressively thought up more and more fantastic lies in an attempt to impress them.

By the time he was in Year 5 he was running out of ideas. It was while he was watching television after school that a brilliant new tale began to form in his mind. By the next morning it was complete. Leroy arrived in the schoolyard and announced in a loud voice: 'I'm going to appear on television! I got a phone call from Blue Peter. They want me to perform my latest rap!'

Some of the girls were impressed immediately but Mr Hughes, the teacher on duty, wanted to know more.

'Just when is this great event going to take place?' he asked, suspiciously.

'Next week, Mr Hughes,' lied Leroy, a big smile on his face. 'I'm on next Tuesday's programme.'

'Well, we'll all look out for that, won't we children?' said Mr Hughes, willing to give Leroy the benefit of the doubt.

As the great day grew nearer, Leroy began to get nervous. It hadn't been such a great idea after all. What would everyone say when the programme was screened and there was no sign of his rap act? There was only one thing for it - he would have to make up another lie to get himself out of the mess. Looking disappointed, he arrived at school on the Monday morning and announced, 'I had a phone call from the producer. They're saving my slot until later in the year. They're going to do a whole feature on rap music.'

Leroy's classmates were very sympathetic but Mr Hughes was even more suspicious. 'Never mind, Leroy,' he said. 'I'll tell you what I'll do, I'll arrange for you to perform your rap live in front of the whole school. You can do it tomorrow morning. That way we'll all get a chance to see how brilliant it is! What do you think of that?'

Leroy was speechless. The blood drained from his face so that he looked as if he'd seen a ghost. How on earth was he going to get out of this one?

Leroy spent the whole day worrying and it wasn't until later that evening that he thought of a solution. He was watching television when an advert for throat lozenges caught his attention.

'Perfect!' he thought to himself. 'I can't do a rap if I've lost my voice due to a sore throat!' He rushed upstairs to practise sniffing and looking sorry for himself in the mirror.

The following morning Leroy turned up to school with a thick woollen scarf wrapped around his throat. He had rubbed his eyes to make them red and he was dabbing his nose with a handkerchief.

'Oh, dear me! Whatever is the matter with you?' asked Mr Hughes, looking concerned.

'Bad cold, Sir,' croaked Leroy, and he coughed for added effect. 'Can't do my rap with a bad cold, I'm afraid.'

'What a pity!' said Mr Hughes. 'And I've just been on the phone to your mother. I've invited her in to assembly to see you perform.'

Leroy looked horrified. He hadn't said anything about the rap to his mum.

'Funny,' continued Mr Hughes, 'she seemed surprised when I mentioned your slot on Blue Peter. Still, I can have a proper chat with her when she comes up to school in a few minutes time. See you soon, Leroy - and look after that cold!'

With that, Mr Hughes turned away and walked towards the school hall, leaving Leroy frozen to the spot like a statue.

He had reached the end of the road with his lies. There was no way back. It was time to face the music.

Prayer: Help us, Lord, to get into the good habit of always telling the truth. May we grow up to be honest and reliable citizens who may be trusted at all times. Amen.

Follow up: Make the point that people who consistently tell lies are eventually found out. It is far better to get into the habit of telling the truth.

Encourage the children to write a rap on the theme of Honesty. They could work in small groups to produce their rap. Here are some rhyming words they could use:

lies eyes skies	*truth proof roof*	*grow know show*	*dad mad sad bad*
together forever	*school fool*	*give live forgive*	*in deep can't sleep*

Allow the groups to practise their raps and perform them for the rest of the class.

A Dozen Cream Cakes

Theme: Greed

Introduction: Ask the children what they think the word greed means. They will probably tell you that a greedy person is someone who eats far too much. Explain that greed can take many forms. For example, someone who is greedy may always want a bigger house or a faster car. A greedy person is someone who always wants more than he/she needs.

There is no doubt that the boy in today's story was very greedy – but maybe he learnt his lesson!

Wilbur Wallis was greedy. Everyone knew that Wilbur Wallis was greedy. His sister knew he was greedy, his mother and father knew he was greedy, his teacher knew he was greedy and so did all of his school friends. Not only was Wilbur Wallis greedy, he was probably one of the laziest children in the whole school.

In class, Wilbur produced the minimum amount of work, even though he was a bright boy. He would never push himself simply because he could not be bothered. Mrs Evans, Wilbur's teacher, had spent several playtimes talking to him, trying to encourage him to give a little more effort. Wilbur didn't mind; he hated playtimes. He would much rather sit in a warm classroom, even if he did have to listen to Mrs Evans nagging him to work harder. On the occasions he did have to go outside, Wilbur would spend the whole playtime standing over against the wall. It was here that he tucked into his playtime snacks, usually a bag of crisps or a chocolate bar. There was no way he was going to play football with the other boys. What a stupid game! All that running around chasing a little round object! Much better to do absolutely nothing, even if it was freezing cold. Playtimes were all right in summer. If the weather was warm and dry the children were allowed on the school field. Wilbur would find a quiet spot over near the fence where he could lie down and watch the other children running around. It was not often Wilbur got hot and sweaty!

Of course, when it came to Games or P.E. lessons, Wilbur was nowhere near as fit as the other children in his class. He wasn't actually fat, he was just a bit wobbly and he definitely got out of breath very quickly. Whenever possible, Wilbur made an excuse so that he could get out of P.E. He would pretend he had gone over on his ankle or he wasn't feeling well so that he could sit at the side of the hall and watch. Games lessons weren't quite as bad. Wilbur always offered to go in goal so that he didn't have to run round quite as much.

Another problem with Wilbur was that he never listened to advice. His mother tried to encourage a healthy diet but Wilbur refused to eat fruit or vegetables. He much preferred burgers and chips and he couldn't resist chocolate biscuits. His

father tried to encourage him to exercise. He took him swimming regularly but Wilbur thought it was more fun to float on his back and stare at the roof. The school did its bit, too. In Health Education, Mrs Evans taught the children all about healthy eating and the benefits of regular exercise but, of course, Wilbur didn't really listen in class and so the lessons were lost on him.

The warnings were there. If Wilbur didn't change his life style he would have a real problem in the years ahead.

After one Health Education lesson that Wilbur found particularly boring, he returned home to find a dozen cream cakes in the fridge.

'Don't you dare touch those cream cakes,' warned mum, entering the kitchen and pushing the fridge door closed. 'I'm taking them in to work tomorrow. You know it's my birthday at the weekend and it's traditional to take cakes into work.'

'Oh, mum – can't I just have one?' pleaded Wilbur. 'It's not fair – I'm starving!'

'There are some new apples in the fruit bowl,' insisted mum. 'Far better for you than cream cakes. 'Now I'm popping out to see your Grandma for an hour. I'm trusting you not to touch those cakes.'

'I promise,' lied Wilbur, and he stood back and watched as mum left by the back door. Wilbur looked down at Rooney, his pet dog, who was wagging his tail wildly. 'She won't miss one, will she Rooney? She'll think the shop assistant counted wrong.'

The fridge door was open before mum had reached the back gate. Wilbur lifted the lid of the cake box and his eyes lit up with delight. He was spoilt for choice! Which one should he go for? He took out a dark chocolate éclair and closed the fridge door. It was delicious! The cream oozed out as soon as he bit into the crumbly pastry. The problem was – it didn't last long. It was gone within seconds and Wilbur was still hungry.

'Perhaps just one more,' Wilbur thought to himself. 'Better to leave an even number in the box.'

Rooney wagged his tail and waited for crumbs as Wilbur devoured a vanilla slice. The fruit trifle was next and that was followed by a strawberry tart. Soon there were just three cakes left in the box and Wilbur was beginning to feel guilty. What could he do? Mum would go mad! He stared down at Rooney and then an idea came into his mind. He opened the fridge door and pulled the cake box onto the floor. He smeared a bit of cream onto the fur around Rooney's mouth and then he grabbed two more cakes from the box and took them up to his bedroom. Rooney could have the last cake – he deserved it for the ticking off he was going to get. Wilbur lay on his bed and spooned a huge fruit trifle into his mouth. He was feeling decidedly ill. It would be a real effort to eat the last cake. He heard the back door slam shut and the next minute mum bellowed in anger.

'Rooney! You bad dog! Get in that basket at once!'

Wilbur smiled to himself and started to attack the final cream sponge.

The following morning Wilbur felt awful. He had been awake half the night with indigestion and he could not face any breakfast. Still feeling full of cream, he staggered to school and sunk into his chair. Mrs Evans bounced in and took the register.

'Now then, children,' she announced, smiling broadly. 'It's such a lovely morning I thought we'd have a little treat. We're all going for a cross-country run! Won't that be wonderful!'

Wilbur's mouth dropped open, his face turned green and he rushed out of the classroom and disappeared into the boys' toilets!

Prayer: Dear Lord, sometimes we are greedy and want more than we need. Teach us to follow your example and be satisfied with the many gifts that you have given us. May we always think of others who have to go without such essentials as food and shelter and may we do whatever we can to help those who are less fortunate. Amen.

Follow up: The children could design posters to encourage healthy eating. The posters could then be displayed around school.

Ask the children to find out why fruit and vegetables are so good for them. Also, can they find out which foods are particularly harmful.

The New Teacher

Theme: Appearance can be deceptive

> **Introduction:** Sometimes people are very quick to make judgements without being fully informed of the facts. First impressions are often wrong and it is difficult to know what someone is really like without actually getting to know the person. Appearances can be deceptive. Someone might appear to be charming but turn out to be mean and nasty. Conversely, someone might appear to be strict and severe yet turn out to be kind and helpful. Perhaps the children in today's story should have waited before making their judgement about the new teacher.

'I'm not going to like her!' insisted Andrew, as he slammed the front door and marched down the front path towards the gate. 'She visited our class before the Christmas holidays and she didn't smile once. I know I'm not going to like her!'

'You've got to give her a chance,' said Chloe, Andrew's older sister, although secretly she also thought that the new teacher had looked very fierce. 'You've only seen her once and she didn't even speak to you.'

'I want Mrs Hughes back,' moaned Andrew. 'I liked Mrs Hughes and I don't see why she had to leave.'

'You know why she left,' said Chloe, wearily. 'She's having a baby, isn't she? Besides, she'll be coming back to work after the summer holiday.'

'That's no good,' yelled Andrew, waving his hands in the air. 'I won't be in her class after the summer holiday, will I? Knowing my luck, that new dragon will probably move up to the next class with me!'

It was no use. Whatever Chloe said would have no effect on her brother. He had made up his mind that he was not going to like his new teacher and nothing was going to change it! Chloe gave a resigned sigh, put her hands in her pockets and trudged through the gate after Andrew, who had already set off along the road, muttering loudly to himself.

The nine o-clock bell rang and all the children stood still in the playground. Mr Hanson, the duty teacher, blew his whistle and the children moved to their lines. She was there, waiting at the front of the line, her hands on her hips, her nose in the air like an army Sergeant Major.

'Hurry up, children!' snapped Miss Snipe. 'Two straight lines and no talking whatsoever!'

Andrew frowned and took his position behind Frederick Fitton, a large boy who hid him from view.

'Stand up straight, that boy!' commanded the teacher.

To his horror, Andrew realised that Miss Snipe was referring to him. He stiffened like a statue and stared straight ahead. No one dared to utter a sound as

they filed silently past the dreaded Miss Snipe and through the school entrance.

'I like well mannered children who work hard,' explained Miss Snipe, after school assembly. 'If you behave well and do your best we'll get on just fine!'

To be fair, Andrew found the first lesson quite interesting. It was literacy hour and Miss Snipe was talking about good story openings. Andrew liked writing stories and he was soon answering questions with enthusiasm. He was particularly pleased when Miss Snipe read out the opening to Andrew's favourite Harry Potter book. He hadn't expected Miss Snipe to like Harry Potter. The children were set to work writing their own openings to a choice of story titles. Andrew was even more pleased when, at the end of the lesson, Miss Snipe chose him to read out one of his story openings. He chose his opening for 'Alien Landing' and read with great expression.

'An excellent opening!' enthused Miss Snipe, and Andrew's faced blushed with pride. Perhaps the new teacher was not going to be so bad after all.

At the end of the day Andrew waited at the school gates for Chloe, his sister. She skipped along the path and joined him for the short walk home.

'Well, how was the dragon?' asked Chloe, fearing the worst.

'She was great!' replied Andrew, cheerfully. 'Not a dragon at all! I've had a really good day!'

Chloe stopped in surprise and stared at her younger brother. 'After all that fuss!' she said, smiling. 'And to think - you were in such a bad mood this morning!'

'Bad mood?' questioned Andrew. 'I think you've made a mistake there, Chloe. I wasn't in a bad mood. I suppose it just goes to show that appearances can be deceptive. You know Chloe,' continued Andrew, seriously, 'you really must learn not to judge people by the way they look!'

And he walked off, leaving his sister standing on the pavement with her mouth wide open in amazement!

Prayer: Lord, may we never jump to conclusions and judge people by the way they look rather than the way they behave. Teach us to be sensible and tolerant. May we appreciate that different people have different views and beliefs and may we always show courtesy and respect. Amen.

Follow up: You may wish to remind the children about the dangers of talking to strangers. A stranger may appear to be kind and friendly yet may be out to cause harm. Go through the rules of how children should react if approached:

- Move away immediately.
- Make as much noise as possible.
- Tell a responsible adult as soon as possible.

Can the children think of any examples from nature where appearances might be deceptive?

e.g. poisonous plants; animals that look harmless; quicksands etc.

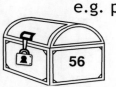

56

Teamwork

Theme: The importance of being part of a team

> **Introduction:** Ask the children: Which is your favourite football/rugby team? You might mention your own favourite team. Ask about favourite players and ask for reasons why a particular player was chosen. Make the point that although teams are made up of highly skilled individuals, it is the way they play together that is important. Players have to consider each other and work together as a team if the club is to be successful. Of course, this is not only true in sport, it applies to many areas of life.

Why was the teacher always going on about teamwork? Jason couldn't see the point. He could do things far more quickly and efficiently on his own and yet Mr Yates was always stressing the importance of working as part of a team. That very morning, for example, Jason's class had been writing mystery stories and Mr Yates had split the children into groups of four so that the children could share ideas and plan together. It was hopeless. Jason new exactly what he wanted to write and he hadn't liked any of the ideas put forward by other members of his group. It had ended in an argument and Jason had sulked when he hadn't got his own way. It was strange, really, because all of the other groups seemed to work together really well. Still, Jason knew he was right and he was glad when the teacher moved him out of the group and set him to work on his own.

Jason enjoyed art but he had a horrible feeling it was his turn to stay behind and help clear up.

'Stop what you are doing, everyone,' announced Mr Yates. 'The bell is about to sound. Now, I want four people to stay behind for a few minutes this playtime and wash up all the brushes and containers.'

Most of the children sat up straight and folded their arms. They loved helping the teacher. Jason slid a little further down his chair and hoped that Mr Yates would miss him out.

'Let me look on my list,' continued Mr Yates, taking a large piece of paper from the class register. 'Right, Emma, Ayesha, Adil and Jason. Will you stay behind and get the job done efficiently. It should only take you five minutes.'
Jason gave a loud tut and Mr Yates put down his list and glared at him.

'I'm sorry - is there a problem, Jason?'

Jason looked a bit embarrassed but he said, 'I don't really like clearing up, Mr Yates, but if I've got to, I don't need them to help me.' He jerked his head towards the other three children.

Mr Yates looked as if he was about to explode. However, he took a deep breath and said in a very calm voice, 'Well, I'll tell you what, Jason - we'll compromise. You've still got to do the job but, as you don't like being part of our team, you can do it all on your own!'

The teacher dismissed the rest of the class, leaving Jason to stare in despair at the heap of dirty pots and brushes. The job took ages. He completely missed playtime and still had his hands in the sink when the children arrived back inside. Mr Yates smiled to himself and left Jason to finish while he read a story to the rest of the class.

Jason was a good football player. He was fast and he was skilful. The problem was that he would never pass the ball and he often left the rest of the team feeling really frustrated. It was the Tuesday before an important game and Mr Yates was holding a lunchtime practice. He had divided the children into attack and defence. The defence were well on top because whenever Jason received the ball he refused to release it again.

'Cross the ball! Pass it!' shouted Mr Yates, but Jason took no notice. He ran straight at the defenders until one of them took it off him.

After ten minutes, Mr Yates stopped the game and called the players together. 'Jason,' he said, wearily, 'how many times do I have to tell you? There are eleven players in the team. Why won't you pass to any of them?'

'They're no good,' growled Jason, as the others scowled at him. 'I could do better on my own.'

'Fine!' snapped Mr Yates. 'In that case we'll reorganise the game!' And he took the remaining players from Jason's side and put them into defence. 'Right, off we go again!' he announced, and he blew his whistle to restart the game.

They lined up ready for kick off - ten players on one side and Jason on the other!

'It's not fair!' moaned Jason. 'I don't stand a chance!'

For the next five minutes Jason chased around the field like a mad bull. He couldn't get anywhere near the ball and he eventually sank to his knees in exhaustion.

Mr Yates walked across and stood over the slumped boy. The other children gathered round and stared at Jason. 'Well, that was a great success, wasn't it, Jason? Perhaps now you see the importance of teamwork!'

Jason did see the importance of teamwork - but he was too breathless to make any reply.

'Time to take the goalposts down,' said the teacher. 'We need to get back to class. Jason - you can do that job today!'

'I can't take them down on my own,' gasped Jason. 'I'll need some help, Mr Yates.'

'Some help?' repeated the teacher. 'You need a team of helpers to take the posts down, do you? What a surprise, Jason! I'll tell you what - you make your way back to class and I'll choose some other children for the job. But perhaps in future you'll give a little bit more thought to teamwork. What do you think, Jason?'

Jason nodded and stood up slowly. 'Yes, Mr Yates,' he said, quietly. 'I'll do that. I really think I need to be part of the team!'

The other children let out a loud cheer as Jason wobbled shakily across the school field.

58

Prayer: Lord, we are all team members. Help us to take account of those around us and to appreciate the value of teamwork. Sometimes we can be selfish and want to do everything for our own benefit. We ask that you teach us to live our lives as a loyal and true member of your wonderful team. Amen.

Follow up: Develop the idea of the school being a team. Give the children examples of how the teachers work together as a team (e.g. planning the curriculum, school trips etc.). Talk about the lunchtime staff and ask if the children can give examples of how they work as a team. Explain that the school has a governing body which meets to discuss the running of the school. Ask the children for further examples of how they work together as a team (e.g. Christmas performance, school monitors etc.).

Discuss the way in which teamwork plays a vital role in life outside school - family life, the supermarket, the hospital, the Government etc. Show that in all these examples, consideration for others is of the utmost importance.

Theme: Teamwork

Introduction: Explain to the children that it is very important to have a mind of your own and to be able to work independently but it is just as important to be able to work as part of a team. You could not, for example, win a football or a netball match on your own - you rely on other team members. It is the same at school. Everyone who works at or attends the school is part of the team and it is working and co-operating together that make it so successful. Sometimes you might not agree with other members of your team. You have to learn to compromise to make sure that the team continues to operate well. In times of trouble, whole communities and even whole countries become members of a team. Today's story is about a team that had to work together so that their community could survive.

Many years ago before homes had electricity and running water and before there was any motor transport, a small farming community had grown up on the lower slopes of a steep valley. Everyone in the village new each other and they all worked together for the good of the community. They were ten miles away from the nearest town, which was reached by crossing a narrow, wooden bridge over a fast flowing river.

The bridge was the single most important thing to the community. It meant that they could trade with the town, the farmers selling their produce in the market and buying other essential goods such as clothing and footwear. More importantly, it was their link to a supply of fresh water, for they had to cross the bridge to collect water from the clear spring that ran down into the river from the mountain.

The bridge was, therefore, kept in good repair. It was checked regularly for weaknesses and it was strengthened when necessary. Without the bridge, the villagers would be isolated and the community would not survive.

The most critical time for the community was at winter's end. This was when the mountain snow melted causing the river to swell to twice its normal size. This was when the bridge was most under threat. However, year after year the snow melted, the river surged yet the bridge survived - until, that is, the year of the Great Storm.

The warning signs were there; dark forbidding skies and a torrent of rain day after day for more than a week. The river had surged and risen to within a foot of the bridge and the villagers could do little more than monitor the situation. And then the storm broke. They had known nothing like it. The sky turned black, turning the valley to night until it was split by flashes of sheet lightning and attacked by tremendous clashes of thunder. The heavy rain turned into a deluge, whipped by

vicious storm force winds. The villagers were helpless. They could not leave their homes and they were terrified of what they would find when they eventually ventured out.

All day and into the night the storm continued, renting its anger on the innocent community. It was near dawn before the storm finally blew itself out, leaving behind just a steady rainfall as a painful reminder.

The villagers emerged from their homes to a scene of devastation. Trees were down, fences and boundaries were in pieces, houses were damaged but, worst of all, the bridge was completely destroyed. It had all but disappeared, washed away by the raging river that thundered down the valley. A group of the villagers gathered on the banks of the river and looked on in despair. They stared at the two great supports in the middle of the river, all that was left of their precious bridge. They were cut off, completely isolated and without the bridge their supplies of fresh water would last no more than a couple of days.

But the supports were there. The bridge could be rebuilt.

Nathan Block took the lead. He was a tower of a man who worked as both a woodcutter and a carpenter. He had two strong sons, Luke and Daniel, who still lived in the village.

'We must begin to rebuild the bridge straight away,' he said. 'We must move the timbers to the river bank and start work.'

'Nathan's right,' said Matthew Grant. Matthew kept pigs and farmed a patch of land, keeping the village supplied with vegetables. 'The sooner we start, the sooner we finish!'

'We can use my cart to bring down the equipment and the tools we need,' offered Jonathan Smith. He was an elder of the village but he was determined to play his part.

'We'll help, too,' chipped in Ellen, Nathan's wife. She was speaking on behalf of the other women. 'We'll carry and we'll load and we'll support in any way we can!'

A cheer went up from the villagers and they set to work at once.

All through the day the villagers toiled struggling through the mud left by the storm. It was not easy but by evening the main supports for the new bridge had been strengthened and the first timbers were in place.

The following day the bridge began to take shape. At one point, Nathan and his sons had been roped together, the end fastened to a huge oak tree that stood near the river bank. They had waded out into the fast flowing river, struggling to keep upright, determined to breach the water and secure the bridge. Bruised and exhausted, they had scrambled back to the bank after an hour of intense work. But their task had been completed successfully. One more day and the bridge would be complete.

And so it was. By noon next day the bridge was rebuilt. Nathan and his sons were the first to tread the new timbers. They stood proudly in the middle of the bridge and turned to the watching crowd.

'To the bridge!' they shouted, raising their arms in triumph.

'To the bridge!' returned the villagers, and a great cheer went up.

The community was saved. The bridge was rebuilt. The proud villagers would continue to thrive.

Prayer: Lord, help us to be a part of your team. Help us to be loyal and true; may we be kind and considerate to others and do all we can to help those who are less fortunate. As we live our daily lives, may we never forget your teaching and may we always follow in your footsteps. Amen.

Follow up: Discuss the concept of compromise. Compromise is not always easy - particularly if you are convinced that you are right! However, compromise is essential if any team is to operate successfully. See if the children can make up scenarios where compromise is necessary: a) at home b) at school c) in a situation with their friends.

Most children follow a team - football, rugby, cricket - even a pop group can be considered to be a team! Ask the children to produce an A4 Fact Sheet about their favourite team.

Lucy's Snowman

Theme: The Seasons - Winter

> **Introduction:** Obviously, this story is best kept for use during a cold spell or, better still, a snowy day. Begin by asking the children to put their hands up if they like snow. Ask, 'Why do you like snow? What is so special about it?' Listen to and discuss the answers given. Take the opportunity to remind the children that they should be careful when throwing snowballs - they can be dangerous. Ask the children if they can think of any people who will not like the snow. Again, discuss answers given.
>
> Explain that today's story is about a little girl called Lucy who attends a primary school just like ours - and she couldn't wait for the snow to arrive!

The weather forecast had been promising snow since Monday but each morning Lucy woke up disappointed. The most annoying thing was that in other parts of the country the snow had arrived. Lucy had seen the pictures on the news - hills, fields and towns covered in a white blanket, cars slipping and sliding, children enjoying themselves. It wasn't fair! Why did Lucy have to live in the only part of the country where it hadn't snowed! It was Thursday morning and not a single flake had fallen.

'Hooded coat and scarf, this morning,' said mum, as they got ready to leave for school. 'The weather girl says there's snow on the way!'

'I don't believe her!' snapped Lucy. 'She's been saying that all week and she's not been right yet.'

'Well, I've got a feeling she could have got it right this time,' replied mum, opening the front door and staring up at the heavy grey clouds. 'Have you seen that sky? It's certainly cold enough for snow.'

'I'll believe it when I see it,' said Lucy, and she stepped out and strode towards the gate.

Mum was right about one thing - it was freezing cold. A biting wind was blowing from the east and a deep frost had penetrated the ground, making the soil rock hard. For once, Lucy was glad to get to school, where the building was warm and inviting.

The first few flakes began to fall about nine-thirty. The children had just finished assembly and were on their way along the corridor towards their classrooms.

'Look! It's snowing!' announced Jordan Jones. 'Fantastic! Let's hope we get snowed in!'

The noise level increased immediately, with excited children straining to see out of the corridor windows. By the time the first lesson started, the snow was coming down much heavier and Mrs Hargreaves, the class teacher, was struggling to get their attention.

'Anyone would think you hadn't seen snow before! You're like a lot of babies!' she said - but secretly, she loved the snow herself.

The ground was so cold that the snow stuck immediately and by the end of the lesson there was quite a covering. The playground and the school fields looked lovely. No one had walked across to spoil the blanket of white.

Just before the bell went, Mrs Weston, the Headteacher, came into the classroom. 'I've got some good news and some bad news,' she announced. 'The bad news, as far as you're concerned, is that we are having an indoor play as it is still snowing so heavily.'

The whole class groaned. Lucy put her head in her hands in disappointment.

'The good news,' continued Mrs Weston, is that you should be able to play out at lunch time, provided the snow eases a little bit and, of course, you have suitable clothing and footwear.'

Lucy cheered up immediately as Mrs Weston went on to warn about the consequences of silly behaviour.

Lunchtime was brilliant. The children charged through the freshly fallen snow towards the school field. After a quick snowball fight against the boys, Lucy and her friends started to build a snowman. It wasn't easy. They could make the head alright but it was difficult to roll the snow into the shape of a body. Jordan Jones and his mates came across to help and eventually the snowman looked quite acceptable.

'What shall we use for eyes?' asked Jenna Morgan. 'And he could do with some buttons to make him look as if he's wearing a coat.'

'I've got some sweets,' suggested Jordan. 'They're a bit sticky but I think they'll do the trick!'

By the time they had finished the snowman was standing proud. Lucy took off her scarf and placed it around the snowman's neck, as a finishing touch.'

'Brilliant!' said Jordan Jones, standing back in admiration. 'A fat, green-eyed snowman! It looks just like Mrs Hargreaves!'

The other children froze in horror and looked over Jordan's shoulder.

'What?' he said, surprised that no one had laughed, and then he turned around ever so slowly to see Mrs Hargreaves standing no more than a metre behind him, her hands on her hips, a scowl on her face.

'I'll forgive you,' she said, 'providing everyone gives you a good pelting with snowballs.'

A great cheer went up and Jordan Jones raced away across the field as a torrent of wet snowballs rained down on him.

Prayer: Dear Lord, thank you for the changing seasons. We think especially, this morning, of winter weather and of the wonderful way it can transform our land. We may enjoy the snow but help us to remember those for whom it is a problem. Amen.

64

Follow up: Winter weather is an excellent topic for poetry. Brainstorm as many words and ideas as possible to do with winter and then write a shape poem. Begin with one word - winter. Use two words for the second line, three for the third etc. Work up to a line of six words and then back down to one, finishing with the word winter.

Example:

Winter
Falling snow
Fragile flakes flutter
Floating, swirling, drifting, twisting
Completely covering the frozen ground
Lying beautifully undisturbed, crisp and white
Until excited children tumble out
Building round, fat snowmen
Slipping and sliding
Throwing snowballs
Winter

Winter Days - Lazy Ways

Theme: Healthy lifestyle

Introduction: It is a good idea to use this assembly on a dull, dark winter day. (Such a day should be very easy to find!) It is also important to discuss John's lifestyle after reading the story. Begin by telling the children that you really don't like such miserable days when it hardly gets light at all. Dull, dark days make you feel that you don't want to do anything. The problem is that sometimes you get a week of horrible days and, if you are not careful, you find that you haven't done anything all week! You begin to feel tired and lethargic and even more miserable! It is far better to be positive when the weather is horrible. Get wrapped up and go out for a walk in the fresh air or take some other form of exercise. Don't just sit in front of the T.V. - play a game or follow a hobby. The more active you are the better you feel. Instead of feeling like winter you begin to feel like spring!

John Jenkins woke up one winter morning, drew back his bedroom curtains and saw - a thoroughly miserable day. It was just like the previous day and indeed, the one before that and the one before that! It had been an awful spell of weather. It was cold, it was dark and it was drizzling. John frowned and crawled back into his bed for an extra few minutes beneath the covers. Eventually, when his mum had called him for the third time, he staggered to the bathroom to swill his face and brush his teeth.

John hated winter. What was the point of it? Why did the days have to be so dark and depressing? He trudged downstairs and plonked himself at the kitchen table.

'I've done you a nice bacon sandwich for breakfast,' said John's mum, putting the plate down in front of him. 'It will keep you going until playtime at school.'

'Thanks,' muttered John, and he tucked into his bacon sandwich, which was washed down by a mug of hot chocolate.

Fifteen minutes later, John was sitting in the front seat of the car as his mum drove him to school. The drizzle had turned into steadier rain and driving conditions were difficult, especially as there were so many other cars on the road at that time of the morning.

'It's ridiculous!' moaned John, as they waited in a traffic queue. 'I can't see why people don't walk to school or work. There are far too many cars on the road!'

It was chaos outside the school gates. John's school was at the bottom of a narrow cul-de-sac and on wet mornings the road became gridlocked.

'I should have dropped you off on the corner by the post office,' said John's mum, as she tried to manoeuvre past a huge jeep. 'I don't see why people try to get as close as possible to the school gates!'

The morning was so dark that all the lights had to be turned on in the classroom. After assembly, the first lesson was numeracy but John seemed to find it difficult to concentrate. He kept yawning and rubbing his eyes and when it came to a practical exercise, he had no idea what the teacher had been talking about.

'You need to concentrate more,' snapped Mrs Thompson, John's class teacher. 'I wonder what time you went to bed last night, John?'

John looked surprised. He had been in bed for nine o'clock. He knew that because he had watched his television for an hour or so before falling asleep.

The children could not go out that playtime. The persistent rain had flooded the playground so that it looked more like a swamp than a school yard. John waited until the duty teacher had passed his classroom and then he took a large packet of crisps from his tray and ate them quickly. He wasn't really hungry and the children weren't allowed to eat crisps in school. Still, if the teacher didn't catch him he couldn't see the problem!

John was feeling even more lethargic by dinnertime and after he had eaten his huge packed lunch he could hardly keep awake during the afternoon session. He was relieved to hear the electric bell at the end of the school day. He collected his coat from the cloakroom and made his way to the school gates, where his mum was waiting in the car to drive him home.

'What have you done at school today?' asked mum, as they edged along the cul-de-sac in a queue of traffic.

'I don't know,' muttered John, yawning. 'Nothing much, really.'

'Oh, well never mind,' said John's mum. 'You can have a nice rest this evening. I've cooked a lovely stew with dumplings. I thought you might be hungry after such a horrible day. And then you can watch some television if you want. I do hope it won't be quite such a miserable day tomorrow!'

Discussion:

Give reasons as to why John was feeling so tired and lethargic.
Do you think John's mum was acting in a responsible way in the story?
What do you think John's mum could have done differently?
How could John have helped himself?

Prayer: We know that it is sometimes tempting to be lazy. Help us, Lord, to lead full and active lives. May we learn to appreciate the value of healthy eating and

67

regular exercise. When the dark days of winter are with us, give us the drive and enthusiasm to live our lives to the full. Amen.

Follow up: Ask the children to keep a record of everything they eat and drink over a three day period. The data can be discussed and analysed in relation to healthy eating. Ask the children to discuss ways in which their diet could be improved. Devise together a simple exercise routine that could be performed safely in class or in the school hall. The routine could include stretching, bending, running and jumping on the spot etc.

Get the children to conduct research as to how their parents and grandparents travelled to school. They will be surprised at the results! Discuss why routines have changed so much.

Theme: Consequences/Honesty

Introduction: Ask the children: 'Have you ever done something wrong and been frightened to own up?' Encourage one or two answers - stressing that you don't want to hear about anything really bad! Ask the children how they felt and clarify what happened to them if/when they were found out. Point out that it is always better to be honest and own up promptly if you have done something wrong. You may still be in trouble but the consequences are usually far worse if you don't own up and then you are found out. Better still, of course, is not to do anything that can get you into trouble in the first place!

It was just one week to the Christmas Nativity performance. The costumes were ready, the invitations had gone out to parents, the children had learnt the songs and those with parts knew all their words. Mrs Kennedy was confident that it was going to be the best Nativity ever.

'Now I want you to go straight out to play,' she said, one morning after practice. 'I have to go back into the hall to tidy up and I'm trusting you to go straight out. Nobody is to come back into class. Is that clear?'

'Yes, Mrs Kennedy,' chorused the children, and they filed out of the door to collect their coats.

Just as they got to the playground door, Brendan stopped, put his hands into his coat pockets and announced, 'I've forgotten my snack. I'll have to go back to class and get it.'

'You can't,' said Samina. She sat next to him in class, much to her annoyance. 'Mrs Kennedy said no one was to go back in.'

'I can't do without my snack,' moaned Brendan. 'I'll be starving by twelve o'clock! Will you come with me Samina? You can keep watch at the classroom door.'

Before she could answer, Brendan had turned round and he was hurrying back into the school building. Reluctantly, Samina turned and walked after him. By the time she reached the classroom, Brendan was already inside. He was rummaging in his tray but there was no sign of his snack.

'It must be in my bag,' he said. 'It's over in the corner by the costumes.'

'Don't go near the costumes,' warned Samina, moving into the classroom. 'Mrs Kennedy will go mad if anything happens to the costumes.'

The Nativity costumes were hanging neatly on a metal stand. The shepherd's crooks, the presents from the wise men and the nativity manger were just behind the stand.

'Nothing's going to happen to the costumes,' sneered Brendan, reaching behind the stand towards his school bag. 'Don't be such a wimp!'

He had no sooner spoken than he lost his balance and tumbled forward into the costume stand. It wobbled for a few seconds and then it crashed to the floor, falling straight into the manger, sending the presents and the shepherd's crooks cascading across the floor. Brendan let out a yelp and Samina clutched her mouth, her eyes wide open in horror. She stared in disbelief at the damaged cradle and the broken wings of the angel's costumes.

Brendan leapt to his feet and looked down at the disaster area. 'Come on,' he said, his voice trembling with fear, 'let's get out of here before anyone sees us!'

Instinctively, the two children turned and rushed out of the classroom. They didn't notice Jessica Broom, who had been looking through the classroom window from the playground and had witnessed the whole scene.

Mrs Kennedy stood in front of the hushed class with her arms folded. She was so angry that her face had turned a deep red colour.

'Someone,' she began, slowly and deliberately, 'has been back into the classroom at playtime and caused this disaster!' She indicated towards the pile of destruction in the corner. 'I cannot believe that anyone would deliberately do something so awful!'

Brendan and Samina kept their heads down and stared at their feet. Samina was shaking and Brendan had never felt so frightened in his life.

'I am assuming it was an accident,' continued Mrs Kennedy. She took a few paces towards the heap of nativity clothes and picked up one of the broken angel's costumes. What was left of the wings fell to the floor and the children gasped. 'I want the person who did this to own up immediately.'

Silence. Nobody spoke. The teacher waited, staring at the shocked children.

Jessica Broom glanced sideways towards Samina and Brendan. What should she do? Samina was her friend.

'If I don't find out who did this,' warned Mrs Kennedy, 'I will have to cancel our nativity play. I don't think we can do a nativity play about baby Jesus knowing that we have dishonest children in our class. Is that what you really want?'

The children gasped again. Brendan's heart was beating fast and he was feeling hot and uncomfortable. Jessica Broom had made up her mind.

'I'm going to give you one last chance,' warned Mrs Kennedy. 'Now who came back into class this playtime?'

Jessica hesitated for a moment and then she began to raise her hand. Suddenly, a nervous voice broke the silence.

'It was me, Mrs Kennedy.'

Everyone turned to look at Brendan. He had stood up in his place and he was trembling, more in embarrassment than with fear.

'I'm really sorry, Mrs Kennedy. It was an accident. I came back in with Samina - but she had nothing to do with it - she told me not to go near the classroom. I just stumbled into the clothes stand. I'm really sorry.'

The other children breathed a sigh of relief.

'Well, at least you've had the courage to own up,' said Mrs Kennedy. She was

70

still annoyed but she too, was relieved. The costumes and the props would be repaired, the nativity would go ahead. 'You had better stay behind this lunchtime,' said Mrs Kennedy, addressing Brendan. 'I'll decide what I'm going to do with you then! Now - let's get on with our lessons, should we?'

Prayer: Teach us, Lord, to be honest at all times. If we do something wrong, give us the courage to own up and face the consequences. We ask that you guard us and guide us for we know that by following you our path will be straight and true. Amen.

Follow up: Discuss the concept of consequences. What could have been the consequences of Brendan's action for the nativity if he had not owned up?

What might have been the consequences for Brendan if Jessica Broom had told the teacher what she saw?

Do you think Jessica should have said anything? Why?

Eventually, Brendan had the courage to own up. What do you think should be the consequences for Brendan?

71

The Nativity Play

Theme: The true meaning of Christmas

Introduction: Begin by asking the children to identify some of the things they like about Christmas. You could even write these on a white board/flip chart as ideas are offered. The children are sure to mention presents (hopefully giving and receiving), Christmas carols, the tree, Christmas dinner etc. If nobody has mentioned the birth of Jesus, tell the children that they have forgotten the most important thing about Christmas and ask them why we celebrate Christmas. This should lead you to talk about the baby born in a manger over two thousand years ago. Tell the children that one way of remembering this wonderful event is through the school nativity play and that today's story is all about a school getting ready for the nativity performance.

It was the first week in December and the younger children of Cobb Street Primary School were getting ready for their annual nativity play. There were just five days to go to the first performance and the teachers were reasonably happy. The singing was coming along nicely, the costumes were made and the actors knew most of their words. Mrs Warren, the teacher in charge of the performance, was a little worried about the number of children with coughs and colds but it was the same every year. As soon as December arrived the whole school began to cough.

Friday afternoon was the final practice and it was performed in front of all the other teachers and their classes. The older junior children loved to watch the nativity. It reminded them of the time they had been shepherds or kings or angels. It seemed so long ago to those who were in Year 6. Once everyone was settled in the school hall, the lights were dimmed and the introductory music began to play.

The three kings walked slowly onto the stage. One of them nearly tripped up as his crown had slipped over his eyes.

'Look! A bright shining star!' began the first king and Mrs Warren nodded encouragement from the side of the stage blocks.

The kings made it off safely and began their journey to Bethlehem. It was the turn of the shepherds and the sheep. Mrs Warren counted the sheep onto the stage. There was one missing.

'Where's the third sheep gone?' she said in a hoarse whisper.

'It's got the flu,' replied a voice from beneath a sheep mask.

'Never mind, never mind,' said Mrs Warren. 'Get on the stage.' She was beginning to feel a bit flustered.

The shepherds followed their flock onto the stage but Jamie Harrison got his crook caught around the ankle of the boy in front and he lurched forward and crashed to the floor. The injured shepherd was about to cry when the angels appeared in a flash of light.

'*Do not be afraid . . .* ' they chorused, 'for a child is born this day in Bethlehem!'

That seemed to cheer the shepherd up and the performance continued without interruption.

Everything was fine until Joseph and Mary arrived at the inn. Joseph had had an argument with the innkeeper during playtime and Mrs Warren was keeping her fingers crossed that everything would be all right.

'Is there room in the inn?' asked Joseph, hopefully.

'Not for you, there isn't,' snapped the innkeeper, and a surprised looking Mary and Joseph shuffled off the stage towards the stable.

Mrs Warren closed her eyes and shook her head. She would deal with the innkeeper later!

The manger scene went well - apart from the fact that the stage hands couldn't find the baby Jesus doll. Mary looked a bit shocked when she stared into the swaddling clothes and saw a large paint brush. Still, the audience didn't notice and she had forgotten all about it by the time the wise men arrived.

'Behold, we bring you gold, Frankenstein and myrrh!' announced the second king, smirking wickedly. He knew very well what he was saying. It came from a joke his dad had told him.

Mrs Warren didn't look amused. She decided that the first king would speak the line when the parents were watching.

The final nativity scene was lovely. The whole school joined in singing Away in a Manger, as Mary gently rocked the paint brush in her arms.

Of course, the following Monday afternoon Cobb Street Primary School's Christmas Nativity Play was a tremendous success. The parents and guests loved every minute of the performance, which went off without one single hitch and the children who had taken part had an experience they would remember for the rest of their lives.

'That's it, that's it!' sighed Mrs Warren as the final curtain closed and the applause died away. 'Never again, never again - well, not until next Christmas, anyway!'

Prayer: Thank you, Lord, for the joy and happiness that Christmas brings. Thank you for the cards and the decorations, for the tree and the Christmas lights. Thank you for the carols and the Christmas crackers, for the mince pies and the turkey. Thank you for the pleasure of giving and receiving presents. Most of all, Lord, thank you for the birth of baby Jesus in a manger so long ago. May we always remember the true meaning of Christmas.

Follow up: Write a poem about all the things you like about Christmas. It is a good idea to begin with a simple list. You can then bring it to life by adding adjectives, adverbs and similes.

e.g. I like getting presents

becomes

I like waking up in excitement early on Christmas morning and unwrapping colourful Christmas presents.

The final poems can be written up neatly and colourfully illustrated.

A Windy Day

Theme: The natural world

> **Introduction:** Obviously, this story would be ideal to use on or following a windy day. Ask the children about their favourite type of weather. Answers will surely include hot, sunny weather and snowy weather. If the wind is still blowing outside, it is likely that someone will tell you that they like windy weather. Ask what it is the child likes about windy weather. The wind can be bracing and refreshing but point out that it can also be dangerous. Ask the children if they can give you examples of how the wind can be dangerous.

Rachel woke up to the sound of the wind howling outside her bedroom window. It was still dark outside and Rachel felt a little bit scared. She rubbed her eyes and reached across to turn on her bedside lamp. The clock on the table next to the lamp told her that it was a quarter to seven. Her mum didn't usually wake her up until half past seven. She sat up in bed and stared across at the curtains. Rachel always left her small, top window open at night and the curtain was billowing inwards, such was the force of the gusting wind. Rachel shivered. She jumped out of bed, rushed over and closed the window and then leapt back in and pulled the quilt around her neck. The curtains settled down but the wind still howled and screamed.

It had started the previous evening. Rachel had been watching the news on television with her mum and dad when the weather forecast came on.

'A deep depression moving in quickly from the west,' the weather girl had warned, a serious look on her normally smiling face, 'with winds gusting up to eighty miles an hour by morning . . .'

'You'd better put the car in the garage,' suggested mum. 'And I'll go and bring the washing in or we might not have any left by morning!'

'It's never as bad as they say,' said dad, assuringly, 'but I'll put the car away - just in case.'

'I like the wind,' said Rachel. 'I hope it blows really hard!'

'You won't like it if there's a real storm,' said dad. 'I can still remember the great storm of 1987. It caused terrible damage - trees down, roofs damaged, electricity cuts and all sorts of chaos. It happened at about this time of year, as well. We don't want another one like that!'

Dad grabbed his car keys and opened the front door. A sudden gust nearly took the door from his grasp and a pile of swirling leaves rushed into the hallway.

'It's started,' shouted dad. 'I don't like the look of this one!'

'How exciting!' said Rachel. 'I think I'm going to like this!'

74

Rachel wasn't so sure as she lay in bed with the quilt pulled up high. The wind was screaming and it seemed to be getting worse.

Fifteen minutes later, Mum came into Rachel's bedroom with a morning mug of tea.

'It woke me up!' complained Rachel. 'The wind woke me up and I'm feeling tired.'

'It's really fierce,' said mum, putting the mug down on Rachel's bedside table. The corner house has lost some tiles from the roof and there is all sorts of debris blowing around outside.'

'Perhaps I'd better not go to school today?' suggested Rachel, hopefully. 'Perhaps I'd better wait until the wind dies down?'

'Oh, I think you'll be able to get to school all right,' said mum, opening the bedroom curtains. 'But I'm going to walk to school with you this morning - just to make sure you're all right.'

The journey to school was difficult. Rachel and her mum wrapped up warm but it was the sheer force of the wind that caused them problems. It was raining, too - not as heavily as it had come down during the night - but it was a persistent, cold rain that soaked them to the skin and made them shiver as they fought their way along the road. It was late October and the wet leaves swirled viciously, blowing into their faces before spiralling into the dark, grey sky.

'I don't like it!' shouted Rachel above the gusts and roars. 'I thought it would be fun but I really don't like it!'

'Not far to go now,' said mum, doing her best to sound cheerful. 'And I think the wind is beginning to drop a bit!'

Rachel wasn't convinced. She held onto her mum's hand and leaned forward into the relentless, roaring wind.

Later that evening, when the storm had finally eased and Rachel had returned home safely, she watched the news with her mum and dad again. The vicious storm was the main story. It had caused terrible problems, particularly to areas nearer the coast. Rachel watched in disbelief as the pictures showed a badly damaged caravan site and a peer that had collapsed due to the high winds and the battering it had received from the sea.

'I suppose we were quite lucky, really,' she said, as the scene changed to one of toppled trees. 'I didn't realise the wind could be that dangerous.'

'Nature can be wonderful,' explained dad, 'but it can also be very destructive. Anyway, let's listen to the weather forecast, should we? I've got a feeling it's going to be a much calmer day tomorrow.'

Prayer: Lord, we know that nature is wonderful but we appreciate that sometimes its power can be awesome. We ask that you watch over us in times of need and keep us from all danger and harm. Help us to be aware of others and may we always be ready to lend a helping hand when it is most needed. Amen.

Follow up: Set the children a challenge to find out all they can about 'the great October storm of 1987'. The Internet is probably the best source for information. 'A windy day' is a good topic for poetry. The children could work in pairs or groups to create their own descriptive poems.

Modern weather forecasting is highly technical - but there are many more traditional methods. Ask the children to try and find out about these traditional methods. (e.g. pine cones, cows lying down etc.!)

Discuss particular phenomenons such as hurricanes, whirlwinds and tornadoes. What causes such extreme conditions? Which regions of the world are most at risk?

Our Team's the Best

Theme: Loyalty

> **Introduction:** Begin by asking the children what they think it means to be 'loyal'. The Oxford English Dictionary defines the word loyal as being 'true or faithful'. Explain that it is easy to be loyal when everything is going well. However, loyalty can often be severely tested when difficulties arise or, as in today's story, when a better offer comes along.

'What was the score?' asked Ben's mum, as he walked through the back door and tossed his sports bag onto the kitchen chair.

'Much better!' said Ben cheerfully. 'We lost 6 - 2!'

'Very good!' said Ben's mum, trying to sound positive. 'You mean you actually managed to score two goals?'

'Well, one of them was an own goal,' admitted Ben, 'but it's still an improvement, isn't it?'

'Of course it is,' agreed mum. 'If you keep training hard you might get a win by the end of the season.'

Crompton Rovers Saturday football team had not won a game in two seasons. It was not for want of trying. They trained twice a week, the boys worked hard and they were really keen to improve. It was just that all the other teams they played were better.

Mr Griggs, the team manager explained to the boys that Crompton was only a small area and that all the other teams had far more players to choose from. Most of Crompton's team came from the same small primary school.

Bob Griggs was great. He had formed the team two years ago when there was nothing else in the area for the boys to do. Peter Griggs was the team goalie and he was also Ben's best friend. They got on really well. Peter never moaned or complained, even though he had let in sixty-two goals in the first five matches of the season.

'It's not down to you,' Ben had said kindly after one particularly harrowing game. 'The whole team has to share the responsibility for the final score.'

All the other team members agreed and the boys still left the field with smiles on their faces.

Ben himself was both the captain and the star of the team. He played in midfield and he worked tirelessly. Ben never stopped running. He supported the attack but he spent most of his time helping out the defence. After all, it wasn't that often that Crompton Rovers mounted an attack. The quality Bob Griggs liked best about Ben was the fact that he always encouraged his team mates. He never complained on the frequent occasions someone made a mistake; he just worked even harder and got on with the game.

It was after their latest defeat that Ben had received the offer. He had noticed the man at half time and Ben was certain that he had seen him somewhere before. He was a large man who wore a long, black overcoat and smoked a fat cigar. Bob Griggs was talking to the boys in the changing room after the match when the door opened and the stranger walked in. Everyone stopped and stared at him.

'Hard luck, boys,' said the stranger, a drift of smoke floating across the room from his cigar. 'You played really well. You were unlucky.'

'Thanks very much,' said Bob, suspiciously. 'Can I help you at all?'

'It's me that can help you,' said the stranger, moving further into the changing room. 'At least I can help this young man.' He nodded towards Ben and the other boys turned to look at him. 'You had a great game,' continued the stranger. 'You could be a real star. If you're going to make it big, mind you, you need to be playing for a winning team. That's were I can help you. My name's Henry Morton and I manage Hilby United. We're top of the league, you know - and we won the cup last year.'

That was where Ben had seen him before. Hilby United had beaten Ben's team thirteen to nil a couple of weeks ago. Ben hadn't really liked Hilby United. Their players were arrogant and they wouldn't even shake hands at the end of the match.

'We're always looking out for new players,' continued Henry Morton. 'You'd have no trouble getting into our team!'

Ben's friends stared at him. The smiles had disappeared from their faces. It was too good an opportunity to miss. Bob Griggs coughed uncomfortably.

Ben glanced around in embarrassment. 'No thanks, Mr Morton,' he said, firmly. 'I don't want to play for Hilby United. I already have a team. We might not win many matches but I still happen to think our team's the best!'

Henry Morton glared at him. He had not for one moment expected to be turned down. He puffed on his cigar and his face turned red with rage.

'You're a fool!' he stormed. 'You're a young fool! You don't realise what a chance you've missed!' And he turned and stomped out of the changing room, slamming the door behind him.

There was a moment's silence and then a huge cheer nearly raised the roof. Ben disappeared beneath a scrum of players as they all started chanting:

'Our team's the best! Our team's the best!'

Prayer: Dear Lord, teach us to be loyal, faithful and true. May we never do anything to let down our family and friends. As we face the many challenges of life, help us to become reliable and responsible citizens. May others put their trust in us as we put our trust in you. Amen.

Follow up: Ask the children whether or not they think Ben made the right decision? What would they have done had they been faced with Ben's choice? Discuss the question as to whether you should be loyal to your friends at all costs. What would happen, for example, if you knew your best friend was going to do something wrong? What would be the best course of action to help that friend?

A Faithful Friend

Theme: Loyalty

Introduction: Begin by asking the children what it means to be loyal. Listen to their answers and explanations and then explain that the dictionary uses words such as faithful and devoted when defining loyalty. You could be loyal to your country, especially in times of war. Many people are also loyal supporters of a particular football or rugby team. Some of you might have a loyal friend in whom you can confide. Of course, not only humans can display loyalty. Pets can be very loyal if they are well treated. The animal in today's story must have been very well treated!

It was a cold, crisp, clear winter's morning and Joe Small decided he would go for a walk. It was just the sort of winter weather Joe loved, particularly if he could get out onto the Derbyshire moors with his dog, Max. Joe lived on his own in a converted farmhouse and so Max, a brown mongrel with one ear bigger than the other, was his best friend. After breakfast, Joe packed his haversack with a flask of coffee, a packet of biscuits and a pair of binoculars. If they could get to the top of White Scar he would be able to see for miles on such a clear day.

Dressed in a warm jacket and wearing a good pair of walking boots, Joe pulled on his woollen hat and opened the front door.

'Come on, Max!' he shouted. 'A couple of hours up on the moors will do us both good!'

Max wagged his over-long tail, bounded out of the farmhouse and ran around in circles until he got dizzy and fell over!

'You daft dog!' said Joe, laughing. 'When will you learn?'

It was colder than Joe had anticipated. The glistening frost looked lovely in the early morning sunshine but the ground was frozen hard and there was a biting easterly wind. Joe pulled up the collar on his jacket and the two of them set off, Max bounding ahead in excitement.

A rough track from the farmhouse led straight up onto White Scar Moor. It was a wild, barren place, a few sheep from Bill Troughton's farm occasionally wandering into view. Max had learned to leave the sheep alone. He looked at them longingly, wondering why he couldn't chase the silly animals but he knew he would be in trouble if he tried so he left them alone.

Once up on the moor, the track disappeared and Joe and Max had to scramble over the rough, rocky ground. The huge stones were slippery and Joe was glad he had such a strong pair of walking boots.

'Come on,' he said to Max, another half mile and we'll be at the top of White Scar.

A hare bobbed up from the rough heather a few metres in front of Max. It was just too tempting! The dog gave an excited yelp and tore after the startled

animal. The hare turned tail and raced away. It was far too quick for Max and he turned back to Joe with a look of disappointment on his face.

A few minutes later they reached the top of White Scar. The view was stunning. Rolling hills sprinkled with white frost stretched into the distance; a winding stream trickled over glistening rocks and bare trees stood in stark silhouettes against the winter sky. Joe sat down on a huge boulder to admire the deserted countryside as Max sniffed around nearby.

Joe was surprised at just how cold it was. The climb up to White Scar had kept him warm but now that he had stopped he realised that the temperature was still around freezing point. Joe took off his haversack and poured himself a cup of hot coffee from his flask. Ah! That was good! He munched on a biscuit and Max appeared at his feet immediately.

'All right,' said Joe, smiling, 'you can have a biscuit too!'

Max's biscuit disappeared in one gulp and he sat patiently waiting for more.

Joe noticed that the sky was beginning to cloud over. The wind had dropped slightly and the sky was filling from the east with rolling grey clouds.

'Looks like we're in for some snow, Max.'

Max wagged his tail. He liked snow.

Joe looked at his watch and was surprised to see that it had turned midday. 'Come on,'he said, screwing the top back on his flask, 'we don't want to get caught up here if it starts to snow.'

He stood up and replaced the haversack on his back. It was as he turned to move away from the boulder that the accident happened. Joe's foot slid from under him and he lost balance completely. He crashed to the floor with a yell of surprise and Max watched in bewilderment as his master rolled over the edge of White Scar. Down and down he rolled, with a tumble of rocks and debris crashing after him. Eventually, Joe was halted by a stubborn tree stump half way down the White Scar slope. He lay there, dazed and shaken, already aware of a stabbing pain in his left ankle.

It was some minutes later that he looked up to see Max peering over the edge of White Scar. He was making a strange, whining noise and he was wagging his tail slowly. He didn't understand why his master was lying on the side of the freezing cold slope. Joe tried to move and he cried out in shock as the pain from his ankle shot up his leg. It was broken. Joe knew it was broken and there was no way he was going to be able to scramble back up to the top of White Scar. His only hope was that someone else would find him.

Max was still sitting near the huge boulder. He was beginning to whine more loudly.

An hour later the sky was a mass of grey. The cloud had thickened and the first fragile white flakes were beginning to fall. Joe was shivering. He managed to wrestle the haversack from his back and pour out another cup of coffee. It was good but there was little left. He couldn't survive a night on White Scar. The pain from his ankle was making him feel faint.

Max wasn't whining anymore, he was howling like a wolf. He was sitting at the top of the slope with his nose pointed in the air and he was howling like a wolf and as he howled the snow began to fall more heavily.

80

Almost a mile away, back down the White Scar track, Bill Troughton was putting his tractor in the barn for the night. As he closed the barn door he was aware of a strange, eerie noise in the distance. He stood as still as he could in the farm yard and listened. What on earth was it? It sounded like an animal in pain. Was it a dog? Yes, he decided it was a dog. Perhaps Joe Small's dog had got lost on the moors. He had Joe's telephone number, he would give a ring and check.

Bill was surprised when there was no answer to his phone call. Joe would always let him know if he was going away for a few days. He opened his door again to be greeted by the same, strange howling sound. The snow was falling more heavily. It was obviously setting in. Bill knew there was something wrong. He made up his mind. He would have to alert the rescue services.

The mountain rescue Landrover drove as near to the summit of White Scar as it dared. The rescuers located Joe easily. They simply followed the howling sound, even though it was muffled by the heavy snowfall, until they came upon a shivering, bedraggled dog whining pitifully on the very edge of White Scar. Powerful torch beams picked out a limp figure half way down the slope below and within minutes Joe was being strapped to a stretcher and hauled to safety. He was barely conscious but the moment the stretcher appeared over the top of White Scar, faithful Max limped forward and licked his master's frozen face.

Max had saved his master's life and the pair of them would live to walk the lonely moors together another day.

Prayer: Help us, Lord, to appreciate the value and the virtue of loyalty. Help us to be true to our family, true to our friends and true to those who know and trust us. Most of all, Lord, may we be true to you, for we know that you will never let us down. Amen.

Follow up: There are many stories about loyal pets. Set the children a task to find out about Blackfriars Bobby or the wonderful story of Gelert, the brave dog who was mistakenly killed by his angry master, Prince Llewelyn.

The children could produce their own stories on the theme of loyalty. It could be an animal story but it could just as easily be about loyalty between friends.

Goodbye Mrs Thomson

Theme: Loyalty/Retirement

Introduction: Explain to the children that when you are a child the early years of your life are mapped out for you. As children, you do not have too many important decisions to make. For example, your parents decide if you go to Nursery, they decide which Primary School you attend and when you have finished Primary School you have to move on to a High School. It is towards the end of High School that you begin to make important choices for yourself. Will you continue your education and go on to university or will you leave school and find a job? Ask the children if any of them know already what sort of job they would like. Would anyone like to be a teacher? These days, people often change their jobs but it was not always so.

Today's story is about someone who was about to retire after giving many loyal years of service.

Mrs Thomson had taught at the same Primary School for twenty five years. It was not the only school in which she had worked. She had moved from Manchester when she married and was lucky enough to be appointed to St. Mark's. Mrs Thomson loved teaching and she particularly loved teaching at St. Mark's. However, the time had come for her to retire and she was feeling slightly sad and a little apprehensive.

The school was having a collection for her. Mrs Thomson wasn't really supposed to know about it but she had seen the letters on her classroom desk. Besides, Belinda Benson had brought her donation in and handed it to Mrs Thomson. The rest of the class had groaned but it was too late. Mrs Thomson pretended she didn't know what it was and placed it straight into her register.

She had a particularly lovely Year 6 class in her final year. Mrs Thomson had taught younger children at the beginning of her career but for the last eight years she had taken Year 6. The children loved her. She was firm but fair, always prepared to share a joke or listen if one of the children had a problem.

'Can't you stay a bit longer?' begged Gemma and Holly one morning as Mrs Thomson was on playground duty. 'Nobody wants you to leave.'

'I do!' muttered Wayne Briggs in the background.

Wayne was the class nuisance - a great lump of a boy who constantly annoyed everyone else.

'I'd love to stay for a few more years,' explained Mrs Thomson, 'but my husband is retiring from his job and we have other plans.'

Back in class, Mrs Thomson told the children how much school life had changed since she had begun teaching.

'There was no National Curriculum when I started,' she said, 'and no tests

82

and league tables for Year 6!'

The class gave a cheer!

'There were no computers, either. It's hard to imagine a school with no computers, isn't it? And I have to tell you - if children were naughty they got the cane.'

Everyone looked at Wayne Briggs, who scowled back at them.

Mrs Thomson's final day was difficult and she had a big box of tissues ready on her desk. Most of the children brought her an individual present even though they had contributed to the school collection. Her desk was laden with plants and flowers, with chocolates and fancy bathroom cosmetics.

'I've brought you a bottle of wine,' explained Gemma, 'because I know you like a little tipple!'

'Well, thanks for that!' said Mrs Thomson, smiling. 'I'll think of you when I drink it!'

Wayne Briggs sidled out to the front and placed something on the teacher's desk. It was badly wrapped in brown paper.

'Well thank you Wayne,' said Mrs Thomson looking surprised. 'That's very kind. Let me see what it is.' She pulled off the paper and studied her present. 'Oh, how nice,' she said, holding it up for the other children to see. 'It's a book of rude jokes!'

Wayne looked pleased. 'It's my favourite, Miss. I thought they'd give you a laugh in your old age!'

The other children groaned but Wayne didn't seem to see anything wrong with the comment.

Final assembly was difficult but Mrs Clegg, the Headteacher, made sure that it was a celebration. She reminded Mrs Thomson of some of the funnier moments of her career, like the time she had been determined to get a netball back from the school roof and had got stuck at the top of the ladder. At the end of assembly, Mrs Thomson was presented with a beautiful set of garden furniture, which had been bought from the school collection. She gave a speech of thanks, her voice trembling a little with emotion. The children sang her favourite school hymn - Light Up The Fire and then they began to file out of the hall.

Suddenly, there was a howl from somewhere amidst the Year 6 class. Someone had burst into tears. The children turned to locate the sobbing - and were amazed to see Wayne Briggs rubbing his red eyes.

'She's my favourite!' blubbered Wayne. 'I don't want her to leave!'

The other children burst into laughter as Mrs Thomson placed a comforting arm around Wayne's shoulder.

Prayer: Thank you, Lord, for our time at school. Thank you for the hard work and dedication of our teachers. Thank you for the friends we make and the lessons we learn. Help us to spend our time wisely and try our hardest in everything we do. Amen.

Follow up: Ask the children to find out from their parents and, better still, grandparents what school life was like in the past. Perhaps this could be done in the form of a taped interview. This would prove interesting for other children in the class. Results could be written up in the form of an account.

Which teacher has worked longest at your school? Perhaps the teacher could talk about the changes that have taken place at your school. Do you have any old newspaper cuttings/reports that the children could study?

Theme: Managing time

Introduction: Begin by telling the children that life today is lived at a far faster pace than it was many years ago. Everyone seems to be rushing around and there sometimes seems little time to relax. Shops are open seven days a week and some of the big supermarkets are open twenty four hours a day. There was a time when no shops were allowed to trade on a Sunday. Sunday was designated as a day of rest. Most families went to church at least once on a Sunday and everyone sat down together for a traditional Sunday lunch. (It might be interesting to ask the children if this still happens!) It is a shame that these traditions have been sacrificed because of the pace of life. Everyone should make some time to relax.

William Harrison was permanently tired. His life was so hectic that he never seemed to have time to relax. William worked in the city of London and his day began early as he had to catch the 7.15 a.m. train in order to get to work on time. It was not too bad in the summer but William hated getting up at half past six on cold, dark winter mornings. There were many times when he stood on the platform at the railway station shivering with cold because the train was late. He usually had to stand up for his short journey because the train was full. A short walk through the crowded early morning streets of London took him to his office, where there was usually a pile of post and a tray full of work waiting for him. After a full day, with little time for lunch, it was back to the station for the journey home - more crowds and no room to sit!

William usually arrived home at about seven o'clock. That meant there was just time to read a story to his two children, Liam and Alice. After they were tucked up in bed, William and his wife Lisa usually had something to eat. William would then sort through his briefcase or spend an hour or so on his laptop computer finishing off the day's work. Totally exhausted, William usually went up to bed at about eleven-thirty, already thinking of the alarm sounding early the next morning.

Occasionally, William had to go into work on a Saturday morning. That would mean another early start, although he could usually get a seat on the train. Liam had football training on a Saturday morning and Alice attended a dancing class on Saturday afternoon. That meant the only day William could really rest was Sunday.

When he was younger, William had lots of hobbies. He loved reading and would always have books out from the library. He played sport - football in winter and cricket during the summer months. He had given both up when he started work. There just didn't seem to be time. The most exercise he got these days was a run to catch the train or a brisk walk every so often on a Sunday.

It was on one Sunday, after a particularly hard week, that William decided

he really did need a walk. It was not a very pleasant day. The sky was filled with dark grey clouds and a steady drizzle had been falling for hours. Lisa and the children were watching a film on television and they did not particularly want to get wet, so William put on his waterproof jacket and set off by himself.

He walked the streets at first, wondering if he had made the right decision. It wasn't just wet, it was very cold. Perhaps he would have been better staying in the warmth and watching the film? No, he would only have fallen asleep! After a while, William remembered a footpath he used to take years ago. It led away from the houses, over some rough ground and down to a small lake. It took him a while to find the track, which was overgrown with weeds and brambles. These days it was only used by fishermen and occasional dog walkers.

After a few minutes, the track widened and it was much easier to negotiate. William could see the lake. It seemed to be shrouded in damp mist. It was so peaceful. There was no noise from passing traffic and there were no children playing or shouting. William began to relax immediately. It was just what he needed after a hard week at work - fresh air, a little exercise and relaxation.

William stopped to say hello to a fisherman. He was sitting on a small plastic stool and was well wrapped up to protect himself from the cold. It was only when William looked more closely that he noticed there was no line on the end of the man's fishing rod.

'Excuse me for interrupting,' said William, thinking the man hadn't noticed, 'but I think you've lost your line.'

'No, no,' replied the man with a faint smile, 'I never had one in the first place.'

'You're not going to catch much then, are you?' said William.

'I don't want to catch anything,' replied the man. 'This is just my way of relaxing. I've done it every Sunday for years.'

William looked puzzled. 'What's the point?' he asked.

'I lead such a busy life,' explained the man, 'that I like to get away from everything for a couple of hours each Sunday, so I tell everyone I've gone fishing. The trouble is, I don't want to catch any fish. I don't think I could ever kill a fish! Sometimes I get up early on a Sunday morning and just leave a note. Two words, that's all it needs - Gone Fishing.'

William was beginning to understand. 'So you just come down here,' he said, 'and sit at the side of the lake?'

'That's right,' explained the man. 'It's wonderful! Just me and my thoughts. It sets me up for the week ahead.'

'Do you know, I might try that,' said William, warming to the idea. 'Just a simple note - Gone Fishing! Thank you very much - and have a nice afternoon.'

William continued his walk around the lake feeling much more positive. Strangely, he passed a lady who was sitting staring at the water. She, too held a rod without any fishing line. He didn't bother to say anything. He assumed she'd left a note at home.

Everyone needed time to themselves, time to unwind and relax. From now on, William was determined to begin a new hobby. He was going to begin fishing - without a fishing line!

86

Prayer: Lord, our modern world seems to be growing more and more hectic. We know that work is important and we ask that you help us to try our hardest and do our best in everything we do. Yet, as we live our busy lives, help us to find time for relaxation and quiet thought. In this way, may we never lose sight of the truly important things in life. Amen.

Follow up: Discuss with the children how they find time to relax. Some hobbies, such as sport or dancing, are very energetic. Do such hobbies count as relaxation? Hold a survey to find out which is the most popular hobby.

Discuss reasons why the pace of life today is so much more hectic than in the past. Watching too much television is often criticised but watching selected programmes can be a good form of relaxation. Discuss how a sensible balance can be achieved.

Pete's New Friends

Theme: Friendship

Introduction: Choose a confident child and ask him/her to name one of his/her best friends. Ask the child why he/she chose that person - what quality does the person have that makes a good friend. Ask the other children what qualities they look for in a friend. It is unlikely that anyone will tell you that they choose a friend because of the way someone looks. Personality and the way in which they behave are the qualities people look for when choosing a friend. Sometimes you can make a mistake and be attracted to people because you think they look cool but you learn very quickly what a person is really like.

There is a saying that old friends are the best friends. Perhaps that is well illustrated in today's story.

Pete had more or less kept the same group of friends since he had started school. He could still remember his first day in Reception Class. Mrs Thomas had sat him next to Joe Harrison and the boys hit it off straight away. Lucy and Gemma had been on the same table. Pete already knew Lucy as she lived just a few doors away in his street and their mum's were good friends. Now that they were in Year 6 they were still grouped together and they all got on really well. They worked hard, they looked after each other and they seldom got into trouble. There was no doubt about it - they were a good group of friends.

One warm lunch time, the four friends were sitting on the school field talking together. Another group of children from Year 6 were messing around nearby. Jordan Jackson seemed to be the group leader. Jacko, as he was known, liked to be the centre of attention. He obviously had too much pocket money as he seemed to have a different hair style every week. He brought an expensive mobile phone into school, even though they were not allowed. Gemma thought he was a real show off. She couldn't understand why some of the other children fussed around him. She was surprised therefore, to find that Pete seemed impressed.

'I wish I was in with Jacko's group,' he said, watching the boy with envy. 'Everyone likes Jacko. He's really cool.'

'Cool?' repeated Joe, sarcastically. 'He's an egghead, if you ask me. Look at the way he's dancing around like a monkey!'

'They're all going off to the cinema on Friday night,' said Pete, ignoring his friend completely. 'I think I'll ask him if I can go along.'

'They're trouble, that group,' warned Lucy. 'If you take my advice you'll keep well away from them!'

Pete did not take Lucy's advice. Before the lunchtime bell sounded he sidled up to the group, trying to catch their attention.

88

'Hi, Jacko,' he said casually. 'Any chance I could come to the cinema with you on Friday.'

Jacko stopped and glanced at his friends. 'I don't think so,' he said, looking Pete up and down. 'Not until you do something with that hair style!'

Pete turned and walked away in disappointment.

'What did he say?' asked Joe, as Pete rejoined his friends.

'He said he'd think about it,' lied Pete.

The following morning, Pete turned up at school with his hair gelled back. It didn't look quite right but he was sure it would impress Jacko and his group. Pete's friends stared at him in dismay.

Pete ran across to Jacko as soon as he saw him in the playground. Elliot and Mel, two of Jacko's group started to giggle.

'How about Friday?' asked Pete, making a point of brushing his fingers through his gelled hair. 'Can I come along?'

Again Jacko made a great show of looking him up and down. He glanced at Elliot and Mel and then said, 'I don't think so, Pete. Not until you get yourself a decent pair of trainers. The ones you're wearing are awful. You need to get yourself a designer label, like mine!'

Elliot and Mel sniggered and pointed as Pete walked off with his head down.

That evening, Pete raided his money box and went to the local supermarket to buy the best pair of trainers he could afford. With gelled hair and fancy trainers, Jacko was sure to let him join the group.

It wasn't to be. The following day Jacko asked him what music he listened to and was scathing when it didn't match his choice. 'You haven't even got a personal C.D.,' he mocked, taking his own expensive player from his pocket. 'And what do you watch on television? Not that children's rubbish, I hope?'

Each time Jacko made a comment his friends giggled and sniggered and pointed. Pete was beginning to feel humiliated. Perhaps it hadn't been such a good idea to approach Jacko in the first place. Perhaps they wouldn't make good friends after all, even if they did look cool.

Pete turned and walked away, his face red with embarrassment. He glanced up to see Lucy, Joe and Gemma staring at him. What must they be thinking? He looked a right idiot with his gelled hair and fancy trainers. He started to walk off in the opposite direction.

'Hey, Pete!' shouted a friendly voice. 'Where are you off to?'

Pete turned to face Joe.

'Aren't we good enough for you anymore?'

'You're too good for me,' said Pete, quietly. 'I've been a bit stupid, haven't I?'

'Yes, you have!' said Gemma, truthfully. 'But we're still your friends - if you want us?'

Pete's face broke into a smile. He ruffled his gelled hair so that it stuck up like a clown's wig. 'Yes, please,' he said, running over. 'I could do with some true friends!'

'My dad always says old friends are the best friends,' said Sam. 'You need to remember it in future, Pete.'

89

'I'll remember it,' said Pete, gratefully, and he turned to take a last look at Jacko, who was still dancing up and down like a monkey.

Prayer: Dear Lord, friends are truthful, kind and considerate. Friends care for each other and never say or do anything that could be hurtful. Friends are sensitive and always willing to listen in times of trouble. Friends are always there when you need them. Thank you, Lord, for being our true friend. Amen.

Follow up: The children could write their own stories entitled A Friend in Need. As a starting point, hold a class discussion to think of different scenarios for such a story. Collect ideas onto a whiteboard or flip chart.

The children could write friendship poems. For example, each line could begin with the words: '*A friend is . . .*'

> e.g. *A friend is someone who will always be there in times of trouble.*
> *A friend is . . .*

Alternatively, compose a class poem using the same approach.

Saving Charlie

Theme: Bravery/Courage

Introduction: Begin by asking the children if any of them have ever had to be brave. Maybe someone has been in hospital for an operation. Maybe you have just had to be brave when you have visited the dentist! Choose someone to tell you how he/she felt when facing his/her ordeal. Of course, you can still feel scared when being brave.

Sometimes, a person can become famous for a brave act but there must be people who are being brave every single day. Perhaps even now, as we are here in assembly, someone somewhere is involved in an act of tremendous bravery - and we may never get to know about it.

Today's story is set during the Second World War and it is all about an elderly lady called Annie Gregson and her cat, Charlie.

Annie Gregson had lived in the East End of London all her life. She had been born in the East End of London, she had gone to school in the East End of London and when she had got married to Ernest, she had lived and worked in the East End of London. Annie had long since retired. She was eighty two years old when the Second World War broke out and, although her sister Joan had tried to persuade her to move down to Devon, Annie was determined to stay put, where she belonged - in the East End of London.

Ernest had died some years ago and Annie lived alone with just her striped tabby cat Charlie for company. Annie loved Charlie. He was named after her favourite film star, Charlie Chaplin and, just like the famous actor, he walked with a lopsided limp, having been run over by a London bus. In truth, Charlie was a really clumsy, accident-prone animal. He had the end of his tail missing where he got it trapped in the fishmonger's door when trying to escape with a fillet of haddock; he also had the tip of one ear missing. That was bitten off in a fight with a neighbour's bull terrier. If cats really did have nine lives then Charlie couldn't have many left!

Early in 1939, when it became clear that Britain was under threat from Geman air raids, Anderson shelters were delivered to those houses who had enough space to put one up in their gardens. Annie's garden was only small and when she saw the metal partitions being loaded from the wagon she was not impressed.

'How can I put that together?' she asked. 'And what's the point of it, anyway?'

'It could save your life, Missus,' replied a burly man with a grey moustache. 'Get yer neighbours to help you put it up and make sure you use it when the bombing starts.'

Bob Grant, Annie's next door neighbour helped her put the shelter together. Bob could not join the armed forces as his eyesight was below standard and so he was an Air Raid Precautions Warden. He dug out a rectangle for the shelter near the back of Annie's garden. Charlie jumped into the hole as soon as he saw it and was nearly buried by a shovelful of earth.

The Blitz started in October, 1940. The very first night the bombers came, Annie stayed in her house, listening in fear as wave after wave of German planes released their bombs over the capital. One or two of the bombs were too close for comfort and Annie's house shook as huge explosions erupted nearby. Charlie was scared to death. He disappeared into a cupboard beneath the stairs and refused to come out until the following morning.

When Annie eventually opened her front door, the air was thick with smoke. Sirens from fire engines and ambulances still sounded and the streets were busy with people. Bob Grant was just returning home from duty. He looked exhausted and shocked by the events of the night.

'It's a good job we sorted out that shelter for you, Annie,' he said, stopping to talk to her. 'Three houses in Bright Street were completely destroyed last night.'

Annie looked guilty. 'I didn't use the shelter,' she admitted. 'I stayed in my living room.'

Bob shook his head in dismay. 'You get yourself down there tonight,' he warned, wagging a finger at the old lady. 'The bombers will be back, you can be sure of that!'

Bob was right. The warning sirens sounded just after nine o'clock and this time Annie took his advice. Picking up a woollen shawl and her flask of tea, she called to Charlie in readiness to make her way down to the shelter. There was no sign of the cat. He had disappeared and no matter how much she called his name there was no response. Then there was a knock at her front door and when she opened it, Bob Grant was there.

'You need to get down to the shelter,' he warned. 'The bombers are on their way!'

A steady, monotonous drone in the distance told Annie that he was right.

'I can't go without Charlie,' she protested. 'He'll be frightened on his own!'

'Charlie will be fine,' insisted Bob, and he took hold of Annie's arm and led her through the house and down the garden to the Anderson shelter. 'I'll come and check on you in a few hours time,' he said and, securing the door, he disappeared into the blackout.

It was not long before the bombers arrived. London was taking another battering and the explosions seemed even closer than before. Annie closed her eyes and covered her ears. She couldn't understand why humans were so cruel to each other? Why, oh why did people never learn? Suddenly, a huge explosion ripped through the night. The ground shook and a cascade of bricks and rubble pounded down onto the top of the Anderson shelter. Annie screamed in fright. There had been a direct hit nearby! Was it her house? Had her home been destroyed? And then there were voices, frantic, anxious voices calling and shouting. The door to her shelter was wrenched open and a bright light shone directly into her face.

'Are you all right, Annie? Have you been hurt?'

It was Bob Grant. He was inside the shelter and he had an arm around Annie's shoulders.

Another explosion boomed nearby.

'I'm all right,' said Annie, trembling. 'My house? What about my house?'

'It's still standing,' said Bob, 'but it's damaged. You can't go back in, Annie. It's too dangerous. Bill Hughes's house two doors away took a direct hit.'

In a sudden moment of realisation, Annie's eyes filled with tears. 'What about Charlie?' she cried. 'Charlie was still inside!'

Bob didn't hesitate. 'Look after her,' he said to one of his colleagues. 'I'll be back.'

The door had been blown out of its frame and Annie's kitchen was covered in rubble. It was pitch black. Only once he was inside did Bob dare to use his torch, for blackout regulations were still in force. As he clambered over the rubble in the kitchen, part of the ceiling collapsed around him in a cloud of dust. Coughing and spluttering, Bob continued his search. He was calling Charlie's name but there was no sign of the animal. Bob would have to back out. It was too dangerous. As he turned to leave, a pathetic meowing noise stopped him in his tracks. It was there. He was sure it was there - but where was it coming from? Bob heard it again and he followed the faint sound until he stopped by the cupboard beneath the stairs. There, cowering in the darkness was the trembling cat, its eyes wide with fright. Bob picked Charlie up, unbuttoned his jacket and cradled the cat in the warmth.

A few minutes later, Bob Grant was back at the Anderson shelter.

'Did you find him?' asked Annie, anxiously.

Bob unbuttoned his jacket and a dishevelled head with one chewed ear popped out and looked around. 'Charlie!' shouted Annie, the tears running down her face. 'You're all right! You're all right!' And then looking at Bob, who was smiling broadly, she said, 'Thank you, Bob. Thank you so much!'

'That's his last life he's just used up,' said Bob. 'No more lives left for Charlie!'

Prayer: Dear Lord, thank you for the brave men and women throughout history who have risked their lives to save others. Thank you for the small acts of courage and bravery that we often never hear about. May we do all we can to learn from their example and may we always be prepared to help those in need. Amen.

Follow up: Set the children a research task to find out all they can about The Blitz. Was the immediate area near your school affected by The Blitz? If you are in a pre-war building, perhaps you have access to old school log books. See if there are any entries which give clues to school life during the Second World War.

The children could write a newspaper report about an imaginary air raid. They could invent characters to include and quote in their report. Perhaps they could write about an act of bravery.

A Family Day Out

Theme: Compromise

Introduction: Explain to the children that when you are a member of a family there are bound to be times when you don't agree. This is especially true if you have brothers and sisters. Ask the children; 'Who sometimes argues with their brother or sister?' There is bound to be a large show of hands. Ask: 'Who can tell me something about their brother or sister that annoys them?' If the brother/sister is present, give him/her a chance to reply. Explain that the most successful and happy families learn to compromise. Ask what the word compromise means (i.e. not always insisting that you get your own way/meeting someone half way if you disagree). It has to be said that the family in today's story were not very good at compromising but their behaviour will teach you a little bit more about what compromising means.

The Branch family were always arguing. There was father Branch who always thought he knew best, mother Branch who liked to get her own way and Liam and Melanie Branch who were forever squabbling. The Branch's house, therefore, was like a permanent battle ground. Even Buster the dog would join in by barking loudly, especially when he couldn't sit on his favourite chair!

They would argue about anything and everything. It would start early in the morning when there was a fight about who would get into the bathroom first; it would continue over breakfast about which cereal they should eat and it would grow even fiercer on the way to school when Liam and Melanie would argue about who would sit in the front seat of the car. Mrs Branch always drove them to school, even though the school was only five minutes walk away. Evenings were awful because the family could never agree about which programme to watch on television.

One Bank Holiday turned into a particularly argumentative day. The Branch family had decided to go for a day out but, of course, no one could agree on where to go.

'I want to go into town to the shops,' said Mrs Branch. 'It's ages since I've had a good browse around the shops.'

'I hate shopping,' said Mr Branch. 'It's so boring. Why don't we book into a restaurant for a nice family meal?'

'What's the point?' moaned Melanie. 'We can have a meal at home. I want to go to the seaside. It's a nice day and I want to go to the seaside!'

'I hate the seaside,' said Liam, immediately. 'Too much sand everywhere. I want to go and see the new Star Wars film at the cinema. All my friends have seen it already. It's not fair!'

Buster the dog barked – constantly.

They were still arguing on their way to the car. Nothing had been decided.

94

They were going to carry on their arguments in the car. As they reached the front gate, they met the their next door neighbours, Mr and Mrs Davies and their two children. Gemma and Callum went to the same school as Liam and Melanie but they were not particularly friends. Liam and Melanie argued too much.

'Good morning to you,' said Mr Davies, cheerfully. 'Are you off for a day out?'

'Yes, we're going shopping,' replied Mrs Branch, with a feeble attempt at a smile.

'My wife means we're going for a nice meal,' corrected Mr Branch, giving his wife a scowl.

'I'm going to see the new Star Wars film,' snapped Liam. He knew that Callum had seen it already.

'And I'm going to the seaside,' said Melanie, haughtily. 'They can drop me off there for all I care!'

'Oh, dear, oh dear,' said Mrs Davies, as her two children giggled with amusement, 'you do sound as if you're in for a happy Bank Holiday!'

'Anyway, what are you doing?' asked Mr Branch. He wasn't really interested. He was just pretending to be polite.

'We're off to the new shopping complex by the seaside,' replied Mr Davies, clicking the remote control to the car. 'We're going to spend an hour or so around the shops, take in a film at the new cinema and then go for a walk along the beach. We'll be ready for something to eat by then so we'll stop off at our favourite restaurant on our way home.' He looked at his wife and winked. 'We know how to compromise, you see! Have a nice day!' And the Davies family piled into their car with happy smiles on their faces.

'Compromise,' repeated Mr Branch, as he watched the car pull away. 'That sounds a good idea. Why don't we compromise? That way everyone gets to do what they want!'

'Yes,' agreed Mrs Branch, thoughtfully. 'I'm very good at compromising.'

'It's all right with me,' said Callum, nodding his head up and down.

'Me too,' said Melanie. 'I'd like to compromise. Can we go to the seaside first?'

'I don't think so,' said mum, looking worried. 'I think we should visit the shops first.'

'That's not fair!' yelled Callum. 'I want to go to the cinema!'

'No, no, no . . .' said dad, 'Let's go for a nice meal and we can talk about it . . .'

'Oh, dad . . .' moaned the children.

Buster the dog just barked – continuously!

Prayer: Help us to accept, Lord, that we cannot always get our own way. We have to learn to compromise. May we never do or say anything that would hurt our family or friends. Help us to respect the views and opinions of other people, especially those who are older and wiser. Amen.

Follow up: The concept of compromise permeates all aspects of life. Discuss with the children ways in which they have to compromise both at home and at school. On a larger scale, countries have to compromise – and politicians are not always very good at compromising. Discuss the possible consequences of failing to compromise.

The Miserable Elf

Theme: Be thankful for what you have got

> **Introduction:** There is a song that says: 'Always look on the bright side of life'. The lyrics give very good advice but many people do not follow that advice. I am sure everybody here knows someone who is forever grumbling or complaining. It might be a relative, or a neighbour, or one of your school friends. It could even be a teacher! There are times when we all have something to complain about but we forget just how much we have and how lucky we are. The main character in today's story was one of those people who was always complaining. Perhaps you will recognise him. (Pointing generally) I hope it is not you!

There was once a thoroughly miserable elf called Elgin. He was always grumbling and complaining, even though he didn't really have anything to complain about. After all, he lived in a lovely house at the edge of Elfin Village, he had a healthy family who grumbled far less than he did and he had a comfortable job arranging transport and sales at the silver mine. Yet he always found something that displeased him.

Elgin would wake up on a beautiful morning, look at the sky and pick out the few wispy clouds that floated harmlessly.

'What an awful day!' he would grumble. 'I'm sure it's going to rain later!'

He would eat his morning porridge, made for him by Eleanor, his wife and then he would pull a face and say: 'Porridge isn't what it used to be. It tasted much better when I was a boy!'

He would look at the morning post that lay on the mat and grumble, 'More bills! I'm sick to death of paying bills!' even before he had opened the letters.

Worst of all, he would grumble about his job at the silver mine. 'I do nothing but write letters and make phone calls. Don't people realise what a stressful job I've got?'

He didn't seem to appreciate that the other elves at the mine had to toil deep underground, working their fingers to the bone for far less wages than Elgin. He didn't seem to understand that they operated in cramped, dangerous conditions and that they put their lives at risk every single day. No, Elgin thought only of himself and of how unlucky he was in life.

One sunny morning in summer he seemed in an even worse mood than usual. He woke up and grumbled about the weather. He went to the bathroom and grumbled that there was not enough toothpaste in the tube. He ate up all his breakfast and grumbled that he was still hungry and when Eleanor made him some extra toast, he grumbled that he had stomach ache.

'I can't go to work today,' he complained. 'I feel too ill!'

'Then you'd better go and see the doctor,' said Eleanor, with little sympathy. 'I'm sure he can give you something to make you better.'

Elgin grumbled again but decided he would be better off out of the house. He put on his tunic and berry and set off for the Elf Centre.

It was quite a walk and Elgin had only gone a short distance when he came across a family of beggars. There was a mother elf and three young children. One of them was just a baby. They were sitting on a street corner, dirty and dishevelled, dressed in rags.

'Can you spare a few coins to feed my family?' asked the mother, as Elgin approached.

'Certainly not!' snapped the grumpy elf. 'Why doesn't your husband provide for you?'

'He was killed down the mine,' explained the mother. 'It's very difficult with the baby.'

'Then you'll have to get a job!' said Elgin, and he continued his journey to the Elf Centre.

A little further on he saw an elderly elf on crutches. The elf was struggling up the steps to the bridge that crossed the river. Elgin had to cross the bridge and he was annoyed that the man was holding him up.

'Hurry along!' snapped Elgin. 'Can't you go any faster?'

'I'm sorry,' said the elderly elf, in surprise. 'My leg was damaged in the mining accident. One man was killed, you know.'

'Yes, yes, I know,' said Elgin, impatiently. 'Just get a move on, will you!'

Eventually, Elgin reached the Elf Centre. He wasn't very pleased when he discovered he could not get in to see the doctor immediately but, after a short wait, a bell rang to call him into the doctor's surgery.

'Good morning,' said the doctor, cheerfully, as Elgin scowled and sat down. 'What can I do for you this fine day?'

'Fine day?' grunted Elgin. 'It might be a fine day for some but it's not a fine day for me!'

'Oh, come, come,' said the doctor. 'Surely things aren't that bad?'

'I think you'll find they are,' grumbled Elgin, clutching his stomach. 'I've got terrible stomach ache, you see. I think it's been caused by stress.'

'Stress?' repeated the doctor, looking at Elgin's medical records. 'Yes, you live at the edge of the village and you work in the office at the silver mine. You have a lovely wife and family, as I remember?'

'That's right, that's right,' said Elgin, impatiently. 'I don't see what that's got to do with anything? What can you give me to make my life better?'

'Hmmm!' said the doctor, scratching his pointed ears. 'I think I have just the thing for you.'

He walked over to a shelf and took hold of a large, glass bottle, placing it carefully on his desk in front of Elgin. The doctor knew that it was water but a large label was printed with the words Elfixiar of Life.

'This never fails,' assured the doctor, and he carefully poured the clear liquid into a glass.

'The glass is half empty,' complained Elgin, immediately.

'No, no,' said the doctor, 'the glass is half full! 'Your problem,' he continued, 'is that you always see the glass as being half empty. You must stop

98

complaining and start appreciating all the wonderful things that you have got in life. From now on you must remember that the glass is half full!'

Elgin sipped the Elfixiar, which seemed to fill him with a slow realisation. 'Yes,' he said, and he actually tried to smile. 'I feel better already! The glass is half full!'

He left the Elf centre with a spring in his step. From now on the glass would always be half full! When he reached the bridge, he stopped to help the elf on crutches down the steps.

'What a glorious day!' he said, and the elderly elf dropped one of his crutches in shock.

When he reached the street corner he grinned broadly at the beggar mother and her children. He dipped deep into his pocket and emptied all of his loose change into her lap.

'And I'll be back,' he promised. 'You all look as if you could do with a good bowl of hot porridge.'

When he reached home, he burst in and hugged his wife immediately.

'I didn't realise you were so ill!' she said. 'Perhaps I've been a little harsh!'

'No, no,' he said, happily, 'it's me who didn't realise what a wonderful world we live in and how lucky we all are! Don't you see, Eleanor - the glass is half full! The glass is half full!'

Prayer: Dear Lord, help us to appreciate the wonderful world in which we live. May we be grateful for all that we have. Sometimes we moan and grumble unnecessarily. May we always remember how lucky we are and may we never forget that you are there to watch over us. Amen.

Follow up: It is very easy to take things for granted. We live in a modern technological world in which we want for little. However, is life really better now than it was in the past? Hold a discussion/debate as to whether the quality of life is better now than it was 150 years ago. A good starting point is to make a list of things that are better now, such as medical advances, transport, housing conditions etc. - and things that are worse now, such as pollution, more destructive weapons, stress levels etc.

Mirror, Mirror on the Wall

Theme: Vanity/Be prepared to learn from your mistakes

Introduction: Bring a mirror into assembly. Choose a couple of children to come to the front. Ask each child in turn to look into the mirror and tell everyone what they see. Ask the children if they like what they see! Everyone uses a mirror. You might use a mirror when you are cleaning your teeth or brushing your hair. You might use a mirror to make sure that you are looking your best before you go out somewhere special. If you look in a mirror you see a reflection of yourself. A mirror can show you what you look like but it cannot show you what you are like - unless, of course, you have a magic mirror, like the Queen in today's story.

There was once a Queen of a far off land who had a magic mirror, just like the one in the story of Snow White. The Queen, who had been spoilt as a child, was very vain and she was always looking at herself in the mirror. She would talk to her magic mirror and ask it questions but she did not always like the answers it gave.

One evening she was sitting before her mirror brushing her long, black hair when Belinda, her chambermaid entered the room with her supper. Belinda put the tray down and bowed politely. The Queen thought how pretty she looked and as soon as she had left she turned back to the mirror and said:

'Mirror, mirror on the wall,
Who is the prettiest of them all?'

The mirror clouded over so that the Queen was looking into a swirling mist and then a soft, echoing voice announced:

'Your beauty, Queen, is so renowned
It's spoken of the world around.
You were always the prettiest one until
Belinda the maid grew prettier still.'

The Queen stared in anger and disbelief as the mist disappeared and Belinda's fair face formed in the mirror. She slammed down her hairbrush and summoned the guards.

'Take my chambermaid to the tower!' she commanded. 'Lock her up and let no one look upon her face!'

The guards were surprised but fearing to disobey the powerful Queen they marched off to arrest the innocent chambermaid.

A few days later, the Queen was sitting in front of her mirror embroidering a cushion. She was thirsty but when she rang her bell no maid appeared to bide her wishes. Instead, Edward, her chief minister entered the room and stood before her.

'I didn't call you!' snapped the bad tempered Queen. 'I'm thirsty! Where is my handmaid?'

'Your Majesty,' replied the minister, 'your maid is imprisoned in the tower. If you take my advice you will have her released immediately for you will never find a more true and loyal servant.'

'Yes, yes, thank you,' snapped the Queen. 'I'll think about it. Now leave me alone.'

The wise minister left and the Queen turned immediately to her mirror.

'Mirror, mirror on the wall,
 Who is the wisest of them all?'

Once again the mirror clouded over and the mist appeared. A soft, echoing voice announced:

'Your wisdom, Queen, is so renowned
 It's spoken of the world around.
 You are wise and strong of will
 But Edward is far wiser still.'

The Queen's face turned beetroot red and she banged her fists on her dressing table. Within minutes the guards had been summoned and Edward was imprisoned in the tower.

It was about a week later that the Queen, opening her window, heard a commotion outside the palace walls. She rang her bell immediately and within a minute, Montague, her loyal servant entered the room.

'Your Majesty, how can I help?' he asked, bowing low before the Queen.

'What's that row?' demanded the Queen. 'Why are my people calling and shouting?'

'Since your minister has been imprisoned, your Majesty,' explained the servant, 'no one has been overseeing the government to make sure your people have been treated fairly. Taxes have risen and the people are angry. They are demonstrating against you, your Majesty.'

'Nonsense!' snapped the Queen, closing the window so that she couldn't hear the shouting. 'I'm the kindest ruler they've ever had! Be off with you, servant!'

Montague backed out of the room and the distressed Queen turned to her mirror. As if to check she was right she said:

'Mirror, mirror on the wall,
 Who is the kindest of them all?'

It seemed to take a few moments for the mist to appear. As it drifted and swirled a soft, echoing voice began to speak:

'Your kindness, Queen, is so renowned
 It's spoken of the world around.
 But try to understand somehow
 That Montague is kinder now!'

'Montague!' stormed the Queen. 'He's nothing but a servant! How can a humble servant be kinder than the Queen?'

The guards were summoned and Montague was marched to the tower where he was thrown into a deep, dark cell.

For weeks, the stubborn Queen would listen to no one. She locked herself in her room and kept the windows tightly shut. Eventually, the foolish Queen began

to feel lonely. Her favourite chambermaid, her chief minister and her loyal servant were all imprisoned in the tower. With a heavy heart, she turned to the only friend she had left.

'Mirror, mirror on the wall,
Who is the loneliest Queen of all?'

Again, the swirling mist and the gentle voice:

'You are the loneliest Queen around,
Your foolishness is world renowned.
Now please, before your poor heart breaks,
Be sure to learn from your mistakes!'

The Queen stared into the glass as the mist faded and the haunting images of her chambermaid, her chief minister and her loyal servant appeared in the depths of the mirror. With a shiver of shock the Queen realised what she had done.

'Guards! Guards!' she shouted, wringing her hands together. 'Go to the tower and release the prisoners immediately! Bring them straight to my room so that I can ask their forgiveness.'

And so the repentant Queen had learnt from her mistakes and the country she ruled was a better place for her wisdom.

Prayer: Lord, may we never be too vain or arrogant to seek advice. There may be times when we find it difficult to make the right decision. We know that we can always put our trust in you and turn to you for help and guidance. Amen.

Follow up: Unfortunately, most of us do not have a magic mirror that we can go to for advice. Discuss with the children who they turn to when they need help or advice. Is there a system set up in school when individual children need help on a matter?

Choose a short scene from the story and turn it into a play script complete with dialogue and stage directions. The children can work in groups for this exercise. If the groups are directed to produce a different part of the script it could lead to a complete performance.

The Two Brothers

Theme: Responsibility

> **Introduction:** Everybody has wishes. Sometimes, if you are very lucky, your wishes come true but more often than not you have to work hard to get what you want. Perhaps you have heard people say: 'I wish I could win the lottery!' Well, today's story is about two brothers who did win the lottery. However, one brother dealt with his money very foolishly while the other treated his win far more wisely. I think you will soon be able to tell which brother was the more responsible.

The two brothers could not believe their luck. There they were, as the photographers shouted and the cameras flashed, each holding on to the end of a cheque worth just over two million pounds! Their numbers had come up on the National Lottery and their dream had come true!

Later, in their hotel room, with the cheque already in the safe hands of their banker, they sat down with a glass of champagne to reflect on their good fortune.

'Can you believe it?' said Luke, the older of the two brothers. 'A whole line of lucky numbers just from selecting family birthdays! We're millionaires, Matthew! We're millionaires!'

'I admit, it's only just sinking in,' replied Matthew, sipping the delicious bubbly. 'It should certainly make life easier,'

Make life easier?' repeated Luke, laughing. 'It will do more than that! Life will be a breeze from now on! One long party. Just think, brother - no more work!'

'What do you mean?' queried Matthew, putting his glass down. 'You don't mean you're giving up your job?'

'I've already written my letter of resignation,' answered Luke, and he took an envelope out of the inside pocket of his suit jacket and waved it in front of his brother. 'Only a fool would carry on working having just won a million pounds.'

Matthew didn't answer. He enjoyed his job. He had no intention of giving up work.

'And I've got the new car ordered,' continued Luke. 'A bright yellow Porsche. Wait until you see it, brother! You'll need your sunglasses, I can tell you!'

'That must have cost a fortune,' said Matthew, taking a deep breath.

'I've got a fortune,' laughed Luke. 'Money is for spending! What's the use of having a million pounds if it is just going to sit in the bank?'

'As a matter of fact,' said Matthew, 'my money is going to sit in the bank. At least, I'm going to invest half of it for the future. I'll probably change the car - and mum and dad could do with their house decorating - I'll probably arrange that for them. There are a few charities that could do with some help, as well.'

'Charities?' mocked Luke, pulling a face. 'Let me tell you, brother, charity begins at home! It's your money. Look after Number One, that's what I say!

103

Anyway, I'll need the Porsche to drive to my new house in the country. 'I've seen the one I want; five bedrooms and its own swimming pool.'

'You can't swim,' said Matthew.

'Then I'll learn!' retorted Luke. 'I'll hire the best swimming instructor in the country and I'll learn!'

Time passed and Luke lived life to the full. His picture appeared in both the local and the national papers and he was even invited onto a television chat show. He drove around in his yellow Porsche and he dressed in the most expensive designer labels. He seemed to have a permanent sun tan from all the time he spent abroad.

His brother enjoyed life, too. He took some time off work for a holiday, changed his car for a more up to date model and arranged for the improvements to be carried out at his parents' home. Matthew appeared in the press on just the one occasion. He was photographed handing over a cheque to a local children's charity but he declined to give an interview. It was not too long before Matthew was back at work. The lottery win had certainly made his life more comfortable.

About a year later, Luke turned up suddenly at Matthew's house. Matthew realised that all was not well as soon as he opened the door.

'Can I come inside?' said Luke. He sounded very subdued.

'Of course you can,' replied his brother, and then noticing the distinctive yellow Porsche he asked, 'How's the car going?'

'Going is the right word,' said Luke, glancing around at his pride and joy. 'The bank is repossessing it tomorrow. This is the last time you will see it.'

'You'd better come in and tell me all about it,' said Matthew, and he led his brother through to the lounge.

There was no champagne this time, just a cup of coffee and a biscuit.

'I've got into debt,' explained Luke. 'The money has gone - all of it. I've been a fool, Matthew. It was good while it lasted but it didn't last long.'

Matthew resisted the temptation to say I told you so. Instead he listened as his brother explained just how the money had been wasted.

When Luke had finished he said, 'Perhaps you'll deal with it a little more wisely next time, brother.'

'Oh, I don't think there'll be a next time,' said Luke, getting up to leave. 'They do say 'A fool and his money are soon parted.'

Two minutes later Luke started his motor and roared off down the road in his bright yellow Porsche for the very last time, leaving his brother to reflect on just how responsible he had been in dealing with his own very good fortune.

Prayer: Lord, as we grow up help us to become responsible people with the self-discipline to take care of ourselves and the compassion to care for others. Help us to use our time wisely. May we always remember that in times of trouble you are there for us to turn to for strength and guidance. Amen.

Follow up: Expand on the concept that success comes from hard work. If for example, you are going to improve your sporting skill or your musical ability, you have to practise.

Responsibility sometimes means taking the right action. Explore different scenarios. Ask the children what they would do if they saw a younger child being bullied in the playground. How would they react if they knew one of their friends was stealing things from school?

See if the children can think of their own scenario where a responsible decision is required. Can any of the scenarios be used for drama?

Read the parable of the Prodigal Son to reinforce the message of responsibility.

The Birthday Present

Theme: Responsibility

Introduction: Explain that the teachers in school always try to choose responsible children if they need a job done. This means they choose children that they know they can trust and that they know will do a good job for them. Perhaps the job means that children have to stay behind in class to prepare for a lesson or to tidy up after a lesson. A teacher will never choose someone they think might mess around and be silly. Responsibility is an important virtue. When you leave school and apply for a job, a prospective employer will want to make sure that they choose a responsible person. I think the main character in today's story might have difficulty in finding a job!

Malcolm's mum fell ill on the very day they were due to visit Grandma for her birthday.

'You'll have to go on your own,' moaned mum. 'I really don't think I'm up to the journey.'

'Go on my own?' repeated Malcolm, looking worried. 'I've never been to gran's on my own before.'

'It's easy,' explained mum. 'Catch the Number 6 bus from the end of the road and get off at the park gates. Take the path straight through the park and gran's house is right opposite the exit.'

'I think I can remember that,' said Malcolm, unconvincingly. 'I'll set off straight away.'

'I've left her present by the door,' explained mum. 'It's a glass vase so be very careful with it. And there's an envelope with some money inside to help gran with her electricity bill. Put it in your inside pocket.'

Malcolm collected the present, which was in a bright yellow carrier bag, stuffed the envelope into his pocket and shouted goodbye to his mother as he set off for the bus stop. He was very proud that his mother thought him responsible enough to make the journey on his own.

The bus was late in arriving but Malcolm paid his fare and took a seat on the upper deck. It was only a ten minute journey to the park gates but the steady rhythm of the bus made Malcolm feel sleepy. Placing the birthday present on the seat by his side, he closed his eyes and drifted away, daydreaming of cream cakes and fizzy drinks.

The next thing Malcolm remembered was being shaken firmly by the shoulder. He opened his eyes to see the bus driver standing over him.

'Come on, lad!' said the driver. 'We've reached the bus station. It's time for you to get off!'

'The bus station?' gasped Malcolm, in horror. 'I should have got off three stops ago at the park gates!'

He reached for the present by his side - but there was nothing there. It had gone. Malcolm glanced around, frantically. He got on his knees and looked under the seat. It was no use. The present had vanished. Someone must have stolen it while he was asleep.

'Oh, no,' he muttered to himself as he descended the stairs and jumped off the bus. 'What am I going to do?'

Then an idea floated into his empty head. 'I know! I'll borrow some of the electricity money and buy her a new vase! Gran won't know any difference!'

As luck would have it, there was a Home Store right opposite the Bus Station. Malcolm chose a lovely blue vase and paid for it with a five pound note from gran's electricity money.

'She's no idea how much mum sent her,' thought Malcolm, replacing the remaining fifteen pounds into the envelope, 'so she won't miss five pounds.'

He set off back along the bus route to the park gates. He was quite tired again by the time he got to the park so he sat down on a wooden bench for a rest. The sun was shining and the day was warming up nicely. Malcolm put gran's present on the bench by his side as he watched a group of children playing football nearby. One huge lump of a boy belted the football and it flew towards Malcolm. Before he could react there was a smash of glass as the ball thumped into the birthday present. The children ran off as Malcolm peered into the bag at the broken pieces of vase.

'I don't believe it!' he said. 'I'll have to buy her another one!'

As luck would have it, there was a supermarket opposite the park gates. Malcolm dipped into the electricity envelope and came out of the supermarket entrance five minutes later carrying a lovely green vase in a plastic supermarket bag. 'She won't know any difference,' he thought, 'and ten pounds will still be a help towards her electricity bill!'

Taking the short path through the park, Malcolm arrived at his gran's house and knocked confidently on the front door.

'Malcolm!' said his gran in surprise. 'How nice to see you! You managed to find your way all right, then?'

'Easy,' lied Malcolm. 'There wasn't a problem!'

'Come on inside,' said gran, opening the door wide to allow him through.

'I've brought you a present,' said Malcolm, proudly, holding up the plastic bag.

Just as gran reached out to accept it, Malcolm sneezed violently and the bag slipped from his grasp. There was a crash on the wooden floor and the two of them stared down in silence.

'Never mind,' said gran, 'I'm sure it was a very nice present.'

'It was a glass vase,' explained Malcolm, and then remembering the envelope, he withdrew it from his pocket and said, 'but you've got this as well. It's ten pounds to help towards your electricity bill.'

'Well, I'll tell you what,' said gran, accepting the envelope. 'I've just paid my electricity bill. Why don't I use it to buy a new vase, eh? It can be our little secret!'

'Good idea,' agreed Malcolm, and then with a broad smile he said, 'I know a couple of good shops that sell vases. Perhaps we could take a little walk!'

Prayer: Help us, Lord, to grow up to be trustworthy and responsible people. May we work hard, play fairly and always do our best in everything we do. As we live our daily lives, may we always remember that you are there to guide us. Amen.

Follow up: Discuss whether Malcolm was really irresponsible or just unlucky. Ask the children to give examples of how they are responsible at home. Do they keep their rooms tidy? Do they help to wash up or do other chores? Are they responsible enough to be left in charge of a baby brother or sister?

The Hare's Revenge

Theme: Cheating/Honesty

Introduction: Ask the children if they can tell you what a fable is. Explain that a fable is a story that has a moral or a message. Remind the children about the fable of The Hare and the Tortoise. See if anyone can tell you something about the story. Ask the children if they know the titles of any other fables.

Explain that today's story is a fable. It is a sequel to The Hare and the Tortoise. Tell the children to listen carefully as, after the story, you are going to ask them to identify the moral.

Hare was fuming. He knew it was his own fault that tortoise had won the race. If he hadn't fallen asleep, he would have crossed the finish line well before the plodding tortoise.

'You were lucky,' he said, ungracefully when he met tortoise a few days later. 'If we were to race again you wouldn't stand a chance. I could beat you easily.'

'I think you're wrong,' replied tortoise, nodding his head up and down slowly. 'I think the result would be exactly the same.'

This was what hare wanted to hear. 'A challenge, then,' he said. 'We'll race after breakfast tomorrow morning. Agreed?'

'Agreed,' said tortoise, and he trundled away, hare sniggering at how slowly he moved.

The following morning the two creatures met bright and early in the lane at the farmer's gate. Hare had brought his friend ferret to start the race. It was a cold, clear morning and hare was shivering as he waited for the race to begin.

'Are you ready?' he asked, impatiently. Tortoise seemed to take an age even to reach the starting line. 'Straight along the lane, around the bend and finish at the bridge. Agreed?'

'Agreed,' said the tortoise, yawning. It was a little early for him to be up and about.

'And no cheating!' added hare, who had every intention of cheating himself.

'On your marks . . . ' said ferret, holding one paw up in the air, 'get set . . . GO!'

Hare shot off down the lane, bounding over the bumps and ditches, his powerful legs propelling him faster and faster.

Tortoise yawned again and plodded forward, slowly but steadily forward.

As soon as hare was round the first bend he stopped and glanced backwards. Good! He was out of sight! He had worked out a short cut across the field and he

109

left the road and squeezed under the farmer's fence. However, it was tighter than he thought and he caught his coat on a barb of wire. Hare squealed with pain as he pulled himself free. He turned to see a clump of fur stuck to the barb and he licked the bald patch on his back before continuing across the farmer's field.

He hadn't gone far when he came to a muddy ditch. It seemed wider than usual and the mud was soft and thick and brown.

'It won't be a problem,' thought hare. 'I can easily jump the ditch and be on my way.'

He took a few steps back and bounded towards the ditch. Hare leapt into the air and his eyes widened in fright as he realised he was not going to make it. There was a flopping, squelching sound as hare landed in the soft, sticky mud and sank immediately up to his big ears. Struggling free, hare hauled himself out of the mud and sank in exhaustion onto a nearby grassy bank. He was covered in brown goo. He looked like a chocolate Easter bunny.

Meanwhile, tortoise had reached the bend in the road. He plodded on, whistling to himself and enjoying the warm morning sunshine.

Five minutes later, the mud hardening on his coat, hare reached the stream. It seemed to be flowing faster than usual and hare looked at it in trepidation.

'I'll never jump across in one go,' he thought. 'It's far too wide.'

And then he had a brainwave. If he waded across the stream the cool, clear water would wash off all the horrible mud! Yes, he would have a quick bath and then go on to win the race.

Hare took a few tentative steps into the water. It felt good. The stream lapped over his feet and washed off the sticky, brown mess. He moved a little further towards the middle where the water was deeper and faster flowing. It was then that disaster struck. Hare slipped on a smooth stone and before he realised what was happening he was being swept downstream by the fast flowing water.

Hare flapped his arms and legs but it was no good. The stream was too powerful and he was carried along, gasping and coughing and spluttering.

Meanwhile, tortoise could see the bridge and he was surprised that hare was not already waiting for him.

Eventually, hare dragged himself out of the stream and flopped down onto the grassy bank. All the mud had been washed off but he looked more like a drowned rat than a spring hare. Wet and bedraggled, he made his way back to the lane. Ah! There was the bridge not too far in the distance. But wait . . . who was that edging towards the finishing line? It couldn't be! Surely it couldn't!

Summoning his last dregs of energy, hare stumbled up the lane towards the stone bridge. Tortoise crossed the finishing line and turned to wait for the sorry animal.

'Oh dear,' he said, nodding his head slowly up and down, as hare collapsed in a heap at his feet. 'You look worse for wear. Maybe we should make this the very last race between the tortoise and the hare!'

Prayer: Lord, help us to realise that cheats never prosper. May we grow up to be honest and caring. May we never say or do anything to hurt others. Every day, teach us to follow your way. Amen.

Follow up: Ask the children to identify the moral of the story. It could be that cheats never prosper or that honesty is the best policy.

The children could have a go at writing their own animal fables. A good starting point is to identify the moral first and then plan the story. Why not read some more Aesop's fables and use the same morals.

The Day the Rain Came

Theme: Water

> **Introduction:** As we live our daily lives it is easy to forget just how lucky we are. There are so many things we take for granted. For example, if we walk into a room and it is dark we can flick a switch and the room is lit up immediately. If we need to wash our hands we can turn a tap and get water instantly. Imagine what life would be like without these essential services. Imagine, for example, trying to live without a readily available water supply - no fresh water to drink, no water to wash regularly and no flushing water for toilets. For people who lived years ago this was a real problem. Today's story is set in the past, a few hundred years ago, and it tells of one family's struggle without water.

There had been no rain for more than a month and John was worried. It had already been a long, dry spring and four weeks of hot summer sun had baked the ground and slowed the mountain spring to a trickle. If it didn't rain soon, John's crops would be ruined and he would struggle to feed his family over winter.

John farmed one narrow strip of land that he rented from the landowner. He depended so much on his root crops of potatoes, turnips and carrots. Not only did they form the basis of his food for the winter, they also meant he could trade at the market in the nearest town. A bad crop meant a bad year and a great deal of hardship.

John lived in a tiny stone built cottage with his wife Sarah and their four children. The cottage was part of the agreement with the landowner and although it was in constant need of repair, John knew that he was luckier than some. At least his family had a roof over their heads. The cottage was lit by candles and by a feeble lamp that John had made himself. The lamp depended on animal fat, which was not always easy to get. Sometimes the family managed without any light at all. It was not so bad in the summer but it was difficult through the dark, winter months. They depended on the fresh mountain stream for their water supply. Each morning Sarah would walk the half mile across the fields to the foot of the stream and fill the wooden carrier. It was heavy to bring back but Sarah was used to it. The water would be used for washing and for cooking their broth. Sometimes she made the journey two or three times a day. As the children grew older, they were able to help - particularly Edward, who was a strong, determined boy. There was nothing Edward liked better than to help his father work the land - but this summer was difficult.

John and Edward stood at the end of their plot and looked at their crops. They had grown well at first. The dry, warm spring had given them a good start and the green shoots had flourished. Now, however, they were withered and brown. John bent down and pulled up a potato plant, rooting in the hard earth

with his bare hands to find the crop.

'There's nothing much here,' he said, a hint of desperation in his voice. He held up a few small potatoes. 'They're usually twice this size by now. If it doesn't rain soon I don't know what we'll do!'

Edward looked up to the clear, blue sky. 'Can we not carry water from the spring?' he said. 'At least we could save some of the crop.'

'You've seen the spring,' replied John. 'It's drying up. We need to use the spring water for drinking, not for watering the land.'

Edward knew his father was right. Their only hope of salvation was a change in the weather. That night, as he had done each previous night for weeks, Edward prayed for rain.

The change came a few days later. It was strange because it seemed to get hotter than ever, at first. It was unbearably hot and the family stayed in the shade of their stone cottage. It was Edward who noticed the sky. Late in the afternoon, heavy grey clouds began to gather. They turned angrier and angrier, their colour changing to black. It was as if the sun had been blotted out completely. The younger children didn't like it and Ellen, who was only three, began to cry. John, however, had a smile on his face. He had seen it before. He knew what was about to happen. And then there was a distant rumble of thunder. John looked towards the mountain and a fork of silver lightning split the darkness.

'It's on its way,' he said, clasping his hands together. 'Thank the Lord, it's on its way!'

The storm broke half an hour later. It began with huge, heavy drops, which fell slowly at first. John and Edward stayed outside the cottage and turned their faces upwards to the sky. It felt so good, so refreshing after the constant heat. They did not stay outside for long. A tremendous crash of thunder started the deluge. The rain pelted down, hammering on the tiled roof of the tiny cottage. The land was so baked that it flooded at first, the water unable to soak through the hard surface and drain away.

John did not mind. The mountain spring would be replenished. It would gush down, fresh and clear and life-giving.

The storm raged for more than an hour and then it gradually subsided. The thunder and the lightning drifted away into the distance leaving a gentler, steady fall of rain.

John and Edward emerged from their cottage and smelt the freshness in the damp air. It was wonderful! For now, at least, their crops had been saved. Nature had responded to their prayers.

Prayer: As we live our daily lives, there is so much, Lord, that we take for granted. We forget how lucky we are to have a comfortable home in which to live, to have enough food to eat and enough water to drink. Help us to remember that, even today, not everyone in the world is so fortunate. May we do all we can to help those who need shelter or are hungry and thirsty. May we care for others as you care for us. Amen.

Follow up: Reinforce the message that water is essential to life. Use a whiteboard/flipchart and make a list of all the uses of water. A good way to do this is to ask the children to think through their daily routines from the minute they wake up - e.g. going to the toilet, washing, cleaning teeth, breakfast etc. The children will begin to understand the importance of water to our lives.

Discuss the consequences for John and his family if the rain had not arrived.

How do we get a fresh supply of water into our homes? Where does it come from? Ask the children to produce a piece of research work detailing the process.

Theme: Always be willing to give advice and always be willing to take it!

> **Introduction:** Have you noticed how some people are always willing to give advice? That is fine if what they say is good advice. Usually you can rely on your parents and your teachers to give you good advice. However, sometimes your friends or your classmates might advise you to take a course of action which might not be too wise. In such circumstances you have to listen carefully and decide for yourself whether or not to follow advice. Of course, if you know that someone is going to do something wrong you should not be afraid to advise them against the action.

Barn owl lived high in the hay loft of Farmer Megson's farm. He shared the barn with Plodder, the farmer's old shire horse who had retired from work years ago. Barn owl was a wise old bird who was always ready to give advice to the other animals on the farm who, in truth, he found a bit slow and stupid. He was also a stubborn old bird who was not very willing to take advice from anyone else.

One cool evening barn owl was looking down into the farmyard from a gap in the hayloft when he saw the duck family waddling off towards the pond. There was mother duck and five little ducklings all walking in a line. He hooted twice to catch their attention and then said:

'I wouldn't go down to the pond this evening. Cunning fox has been lurking around lately and he likes nothing better than duckling for his supper!'

'Well, thank you very much,' quacked mother duck, looking up to the hayloft, 'but I think I can look after my own family all the same!' And the fluffy ducks waddled out of the farmyard with their heads held high in the air.

Five minutes later barn owl's sharp ears picked up the most awful commotion. There was quacking and squawking and flapping and, as he watched from the hay loft, mother duck came running back into the yard with just three little ducklings following her.

'That awful fox has carried off two of my babies!' she cried. 'He's probably eating them at this very minute!'

'You should have listened to my advice,' scolded barn owl, and he nodded his head up and down wisely.

Later that evening, Plodder the shire horse reminded barn owl of the news he had heard about the hayloft.

'Don't forget to keep your eyes open for a new home,' he said, seriously. 'Farmer Megson's knocking the barn down next week to make way for a brand new storage building.'

'Yes, yes,' replied barn owl, impatiently. 'I know all about that. I'll deal with it soon! I'll deal with it soon!'

115

The next morning barn owl was looking through his gap in the hayloft when he noticed two of the farmer's sheep escaping from their pen.

'I wouldn't wander too far away,' advised barn owl. 'I understand there's a sheep thief in the area and I wouldn't want you to come to any harm.'

'Thank you very much,' replied one of the sheep. 'But we're fed up of being cooped together in a tiny pen. We're going for a walk across the wide open fields.'

Barn owl shook his head and flew down beside shire horse.

'It's a mistake,' he said, seriously. 'I don't know why the silly creatures can't take advice.'

Sure enough, half an hour later just one of the sheep came bleating back.

'My friend's been stolen,' it bleated, pitifully. 'A horrible human grabbed her and ran off into the woods! What will become of her?'

'You should have taken note of my warning,' scolded barn owl, and once again he nodded his head up and down wisely.

Later that afternoon, Farmer Megson turned up at the barn with two men wearing builder's hats. The men prodded the walls and measured the floors and did a lot of talking.

'I think you should look for a new barn,' advised shire horse once the men had left. 'It looks as if they're going to start work soon.'

'Yes, yes, I know!' snapped barn owl, impatiently. 'It won't take me long to find a new place!'

It was just turning dusk when barn owl heard an unusual grunting noise. Flying down from the hayloft, he saw pig squeezing through a tight gap in his pen.

'What are you doing?' asked barn owl. He landed on a nearby gate post. 'I'm still hungry,' explained greedy pig.

'I'm going round to the bins at the back of the farmhouse. There's always some extra food in the bins.'

'I wouldn't do that!' advised barn owl. 'Farmer Megson caught the last pig that stole from the bins and sent him straight to market!'

'He won't catch me!' guffawed greedy pig, and he trotted off to find the food bins.

A few minutes later the air was split by a high pitched squealing. Owl watched in amazement as Farmer Megson chased the greedy pig across the farmyard with a big stick in his hand.

'Wait 'til I catch you!' shouted the angry farmer. 'It'll be straight to the market with you!'

Barn owl smiled smugly to himself. 'He should have listened to me,' he thought. 'Why, oh why can't they take good advice?'

Barn owl was still asleep the next morning when the builders moved in. A great sledge hammer smashed down the barn door and a noisy truck drove inside. Four men jumped out and set to work immediately.

Barn owl was surprised and confused. And where was shire horse? Barn owl

looked down into the farm yard from the gap in the hayloft to see Farmer Megson leading the old horse to its new paddock.

'I told you to look for a new barn,' neighed the old horse as he was led away. 'You're so good at giving advice yet you're hopeless at taking it!'

Barn owl nodded his head up and down as a cloud of dust filled the hay loft and the walls began to crumble.

Prayer: Dear Lord, help us to make the correct decisions in life. May we never be too proud to listen to the advice of those who are older and wiser. May we learn from your teaching, for we always know that we can turn to you for help when we are in need. Amen.

Follow up: Introduce the concept of peer pressure. Discuss with the children the action they should take if given bad advice. Give a scenario - e.g. a group of children you are with start to smoke and advise you to take a cigarette. How would you deal with the situation? Ask the children to come up with other examples for discussion. Explain that it sometimes takes great strength of character to say 'no'.

_____ Danger - Keep Out!

Theme: The danger of playing near a building site

> **Introduction:** This story is particularly relevant should there be building work taking place in or near school. Begin by asking the children to name areas where it is unsafe to play. You should get answers such as busy roads, railway lines, factory yards, near water etc. As each answer is given, ask for reasons why children should not play in such areas. Ask if there are any specific areas near school which are dangerous. If it has not been mentioned, ask the children why they should not play around building sites. Tell the children that today's story serves as a good reminder as to why you should never play around a building site.

Everyone at Moss Street School was excited about the new computer suite. The building work had been going on for a few weeks and an area of the playground at the back of the school had been securely fenced. It was amazing how quickly the new extension was taking shape. The builders had erected scaffolding and the outside walls and part of the roof were already in place.

'Now, you all know that it is half term next week,' explained Mrs Jackson, in school assembly. 'I want you to make sure that you keep well away from the building work. In fact, I would prefer you not to play in the school yard at all. Building sites can be very dangerous places and I want you all to return to school safe and sound after the half term holiday.'

'I don't think much of that!' muttered Jack Benson on his way out of school assembly. 'Where else are we supposed to play?'

'We could go down to the park,' suggested David Hatch. The two boys were best friends and they often used the school grounds in the evenings and school holidays - even though they knew that they were really out of bounds.

'It's too far to the park,' complained Jack. 'Why walk all that way when there's a playground and a school field so much nearer.'

'I suppose you're right,' replied David, although secretly he was not so sure.

The boys didn't even wait until Monday. They met outside the school gate after lunch on Saturday and they had climbed over and into the school yard within seconds. Jack had brought his new football with him.

'Shall we go onto the school field,' suggested David. 'At least we'll be away from the building site.'

'No way!' snapped Jack. 'It was pouring with rain earlier. The school field will be soaked. Let's practise against the wall. Nobody's going to see us.'

Everything was fine at first. The boys were joined by a couple of their friends and they practised shooting at a target that had been painted on the school wall.

However, it wasn't long before David shot high and wide and the boys looked on in dismay as the ball flew over the security fence and lodged in a corner of the scaffolding.

'Sorry!' said David, looking embarrassed. 'We can come and ask for it back on Monday when the men are working.'

'Don't be stupid,' snapped Jack. 'I'm not waiting until Monday. 'I can easily climb over the fence and get it back!'

'I don't think you should,' warned one of the other boys. 'You heard what Mrs Jackson said.'

'Mrs Jackson's not going to find out, is she?' said Jack, and he jumped onto the wall and pulled himself up and over the security fence. 'Easy!' he said, as he dropped down into the building site. 'I'll have it back in no time!'

What Jack didn't know was that the ball had lodged in a part of the scaffolding that was not properly secured. The builders had been putting it together but had not finished the job.

Jack climbed onto the bottom bar of the scaffolding and pulled himself up. David and his friends watched anxiously. Jack reached the first level easily and the ball was in sight. He edged towards it and the scaffolding began to wobble. The boys beneath gasped. They could see what was going to happen.

'Jack! Get down!' yelled David. 'The scaffolding's giving way!'

'I'm all right,' retorted Jack, reaching out a hand towards the ball. 'I've nearly got it!'

It all happened so quickly. There was a cloud of dust and a clamour of sound as the scaffolding crashed to the ground. The boys heard Jack scream but all they could do was look on in horror. They seemed to be frozen to the spot. The dust cloud cleared and the boys peered towards the mess of twisted metal and rubble. Jack was trapped. He was half buried beneath the collapsed scaffolding and there was no way he could drag himself free. Moaning with pain, he glanced towards the fence and shouted for help.

Adults appeared within seconds, passers by alerted by the noise and the dust cloud. One of them was on his mobile phone calling for an ambulance while another man in a blue track suit scaled the security fence and approached the injured boy.

'He's been lucky,' shouted the man. 'He doesn't seem to be too badly hurt - it's just his leg that's trapped!'

The ambulance, together with two police cars and a fire engine, arrived within minutes. The fire crew soon had Jack freed and he even managed a smile as he was carried past his friends on a stretcher.

David grinned back but his smile soon disappeared as he saw the police constable walking towards him.

'I want a word with you lads,' he said, and he took out his notebook and pencil as David took a deep breath.

Prayer: Lord, we know that we face many dangers as we live our daily lives. May we do all we can to keep ourselves and others safe by following the rules. Help us to listen to advice from those who are older and wiser. May we never act in a rash or foolish way that could lead us into danger. Amen.

Follow up: You may wish to reinforce the message that children should not play in the school grounds when the school is closed.

The story has a clear message. The children could write their own stories about other dangerous places. The stories could then be shared in class or a subsequent assembly in order to reinforce the message about avoiding dangerous places.

The children could design their own posters warning against playing in a dangerous place.

Watching Jenny Wren

Theme: The Seasons/Birds in spring

> **Introduction:** Have you noticed that when you get a bright, sunny spring day everyone seems more cheerful? Spring is a time of new life and new energy. Spring bulbs and flowers brighten our gardens and roadsides; new lambs are born and birds build their nests and lay their eggs.
>
> Today's story is about a particularly lively little bird that is quite common in our country. See if you can guess what it is before its name is mentioned in the story.

Jennifer was sitting on the garden wall watching her dad give the lawn its very first cut of the year. It was a beautiful Saturday afternoon in early April, the sky was blue and Jennifer was feeling very happy with herself - especially as she had just finished school the day before for the Easter holiday. She had first noticed the lively little bird a few minutes earlier. Her father had gone to the compost heap at the bottom of the garden to empty the grass box and the little brown bird had darted from the top of the fence and picked up a tuft of cut grass with its beak. It had only been a metre or so from Jenny and she had got a good look at it. It glanced around nervously, flicked its short tail and then took off and flew in a straight line towards the row of houses beyond Jennifer's garden.

'Did you see it?' asked Jenny, as her dad reappeared with the empty grass box. 'It was so cute! I hope it comes back again.'

'What on earth are you talking about?' said Jenny's dad, looking puzzled. 'Have we had a visitor?'

'There was a little bird,' replied Jenny. 'It was sitting on the fence watching you cut the lawn and it flew down and pinched some of the grass cuttings.'

'It'll be back,' said dad, confidently. 'It will be building its nest. Birds are intelligent, you know. Once they find something useful for nest building they return for more. You keep your eyes open and you'll see it again in a few minutes.'

Jenny's dad got on with his job. The electric mower buzzed into life and he set off down the garden, trying his best to keep it in a straight line. Sure enough, a few minutes later, Jenny's little friend returned. It landed in almost the same place on the fence and glanced around to make sure it was safe. It was mostly dark brown in colour but it was paler underneath and it seemed to have prominent eyebrows. Its short tail flicked every so often, so that it appeared restless and anxious to get on with its job.

The lawnmower returned to the top of the garden and Jenny indicated towards the fence, mouthing as quietly as he could. 'Dad... dad... She's back! Over there! Sitting on the fence!'

Jenny's dad left the mower and joined her by the wall. The little bird glanced around suspiciously and then darted down onto the grass.

121

It glanced around again and then picked up some loose grass. It was airborne in a second, disappearing over the fence in the same direction as last time.

'Ah!' said Jennifer's dad, knowingly. 'Do you know what type of bird it is?'

'I think it might be a sparrow,' said Jenny, taking a wild guess.

'No, it's not a sparrow,' replied dad, as the little bird reappeared on top of the fence. It glanced around again but this time it didn't fly down to the lawn. It was as if it knew that Jenny and her dad were talking about it and it suddenly burst into a shrill song. Jennifer was surprised that such a small bird could make such a loud noise.

'Just like you, in many ways,' said Jenny's dad, nodding his head. 'Small but amazingly noisy!'

Jenny punched him on the arm and asked, 'If it's not a sparrow, what sort of a bird is it?'

'I'll give you a clue,' said dad. 'It has four letters in its name and the first one is a silent letter. Any ideas?'

Jenny thought for a few moments and then her eyes lit up. 'It's a wren!' she announced. 'I should have guessed! They're sometimes called Jenny wrens, aren't they?'

'That's right,' said dad, putting an arm around his daughter. 'I told you she was just like you -small and noisy but very lively and quite cute!'

As if on cue, the little wren sang again, flicked its tail and then flew down to collect another mouthful of freshly mown grass. She had given her show. It was springtime and there was important work that had to be done.

'I love her,' said Jenny, watching as the little bird disappeared into the distance. 'I think wrens are my very favourite type of birds.'

Prayer: Thank you, Lord, for the wonderful creatures that you have created. We think especially, this morning, of the many varieties of birds that bring so much pleasure to our towns and gardens. Sometimes we take the most simple, pleasurable things in life for granted. May we do everything we can to protect the environment so that our birds continue to thrive. Amen.

Follow up: The children could use the school library or Internet to produce an information sheet about the wren or any other town or garden bird of their choice. They could produce their information sheet with sub-headings, such as: Description; Feeding; Habitat etc. They could add pictures or illustrations.
School grounds often provide an excellent environment for wild birds. Discuss what could be done to encourage birds into the school grounds. Conduct a survey to identify different bird visitors. Which is the most common bird to visit the school grounds?

Skip to be Fit

Theme: Healthy living

> **Introduction:** Lack of vigorous exercise for both children and adults is an issue in today's society. Many children hardly walk anywhere at all. They are driven to school, they are driven to the supermarket and they are even delivered and collected from their friends' houses.
>
> Bring a skipping rope into assembly. Ask who would like to show everyone how to skip and choose a child to demonstrate. Choose another child so that you have selected one boy and one girl. Keep the second child going so that he/she is a little breathless. Ask: 'How did it make you feel?' Explain that skipping is an excellent activity to help you keep fit. It strengthens muscles and it increases stamina. If you are brave enough - show the children that you can skip!

Joe and Kieran looked on in surprise as Mr Ellis, their teacher, demonstrated how well he could skip. It was a warm spring day and the children were on the school field for a P.E. lesson. Before break they had been learning about the benefits of healthy eating and exercise and Mr Ellis had warned them that they were in for some tough exercise in P.E.

'I thought he said it was going to be tough?' whispered Joe, as Mr Ellis went through his routine. 'I didn't think he meant skipping! Skipping's for girls!'

Mr Ellis started off slowly, keeping his feet together and jumping just enough for the rope to pass beneath them.

'Easy,' muttered Kieran. 'Anyone can skip! I don't see how that can keep you fit!'

Gradually, Mr Ellis increased the pace so that the rope turned faster and faster. Eventually, it was whizzing round, making a whooshing sound as it cut through the air.

'Not bad,' admitted Joe, as Mr Ellis brought the rope to a stop and took a deep breath, 'but I still think we'd be better off playing football!'

'Now then,' began Mr Ellis, 'it's your turn. 'I'm going to send you to the P.E. baskets in groups so that you can get a skipping rope. I want you to find a space a safe distance from the next person and I want to see how well you can skip.'

Joe and Kieran both pulled a face as they each collected a skipping rope and found spaces next to each other. Joe was hopeless. The first time he tried it the rope wobbled over his head, caught in his legs and he fell flat on his face. Kieran burst out laughing but he wasn't much better. He kept getting tangled up in his rope so that he looked like a Christmas parcel! Emily Thomas, who was working nearby was brilliant. The rope moved around smoothly and the whole exercise seemed effortless.

123

'It's impossible!' complained Joe, picking himself up for the fourth time. 'There must be something wrong with my rope!'

After about ten minutes, Mr Ellis stopped the children and gathered them together. He chose a few of the better skippers to demonstrate and then, staring at Joe and Kieran, he said: 'Of course, some of us are not so good, are we? I've made a list of those who need a little more practice. I'm going to allow you to take a rope home so that you can improve.' And he read out a short list of about five names.

'It's not fair!' complained Joe later that evening. He had just removed the skipping rope from his school bag and he was sitting in the kitchen staring at it. 'What's the point of learning how to skip? It's not something I'm going to use a lot, is it?'

'Skipping is brilliant,' said Joe's dad, putting down his newspaper. 'It's one of the best ways to get yourself fit. Think about it - boxers skip to improve their strength and stamina; so do footballers and rugby players and most other people who play sport professionally. It's cheap to do - all you need is a piece of rope - and it's really good fun. Come out into the back garden and we'll have a practice.'

A few minutes later, Joe was amazed to see his father skipping fluently on the back lawn! He was nearly as good as Mr Ellis. The strange thing was, a few doors away, Kieran's dad was doing exactly the same thing! Joe could see his head appearing above the hedge as he bounced up and down.

'All right,' said Joe. He was beginning to change his mind. 'I'll give it a go. I'll go and call for Kieran and we'll see if we can learn how to skip properly.'

It took a while but gradually the boys improved. After half an hour they could skip reasonably well.

'Look at me!' shouted Joe, as he managed ten consecutive turns of the rope. 'I've scored ten!'

'I just got thirteen!' boasted Kieran. 'But I've had enough now! My legs are killing me!'

'We'll show them tomorrow,' promised Joe. 'I don't see what all the fuss was about! Anyone can skip!'

The following day the children had an extra P.E. lesson. There were no mocking comments from Joe and Kieran this time. In fact, when Mr Ellis asked for volunteers the two boys were the first to raise their hands.

'Excellent!' exclaimed Mr Ellis, as they both passed fifteen skips. 'A big improvement after just a little bit of practice! Now, see if you can double your score by the end of the lesson. Thirty skips without stopping!'

'Easy,' said Joe.

'Piece of cake!' agreed Kieran, and the boys wandered off to find a space in which to practise.

Prayer: Dear Lord, help us to enjoy life to the full. May we do everything we can to keep ourselves fit and healthy. We know that a sensible diet and regular exercise are so important. Give us a healthy mind and a healthy body so that we are ready to meet the many challenges that lie ahead. Amen.

Follow up: Why not hold a sponsored skip. You could call your event Skip To Be Fit! Not only will the event raise money for school funds, it will also contribute to the health and fitness of the children and therefore should be popular with parents. The event could be held on a particular day with agreed targets for the children according to their age (e.g. skip for two minutes, for five minutes etc.). The event could be made more interesting by holding skipping races or group skipping with a larger rope. There could even be a prize or trophy for the champion skipper in school!

A Helping Hand

Theme: Bullying

Introduction: There are times when both adults and children can be far too quick to pass a judgement or jump to the wrong conclusion. It is almost impossible to tell what someone is like just by their looks. There are occasions when people are bullied or picked on just because they are different in some way. The little girl in today's story seemed to be different from her classmates and, as a result, she was treated badly. It was only when one of her tormentors was in trouble that the girl's true character was discovered.

'You're not playing with us!' snapped Carla Smith, shouting straight into Kirsty's face. 'Go and find someone as scruffy as yourself to play with!'

'Yeah, we don't want you,' agreed Simone. 'Push off and find your own friends!'

That was the problem - Kirsty didn't have any friends. Since she had moved to Mellor Street Primary School she had found it difficult to settle in. She knew she was different from the other children. Their school uniforms always seemed fresh and new and they always seemed to have the latest fashion accessories. They talked about the latest CDs or computer games they had bought, or the latest film they had been to see at the local cinema complex. Kirsty didn't own a computer and she couldn't even remember the last time she had visited the cinema.

It had been so different at her last school, before her mother had fallen ill and been forced to give up work. Kirsty leaned back against the playground wall and wished that she could turn back the clock.

'Don't stand there, stupid!' yelled Daniel Brown. 'You're right in the middle of the goal! Move out of the way!'

Head down, Kirsty trudged across the school yard and took shelter in the doorway. She hated playtimes. At least when she was in class the other children couldn't make fun of her or call her names.

Later that afternoon, Mrs Heston, the class teacher, asked the children to organise themselves into twos for a drama lesson. Kirsty watched and waited in embarrassment as the other children in the class sorted themselves into pairs.

'Can we work in a three, Miss?' asked Carla Smith. She had linked arms with Simone and Yasmin.

'There's no need to work in a three,' replied Mrs Heston. 'Kirsty is still on her own. One of you move across and work with Kirsty.'

The three girls pulled faces.

'I'm not going,' growled Carla, edging further away. 'It'll have to be one of you two.'

Reluctantly, Yasmin let go of Simone's arm and went to work with Kirsty.

'Thanks,' said Kirsty, giving Yasmin a friendly smile.

'It's not out of choice,' snapped Yasmin. 'You were the only one left!'

Kirsty was always pleased when the weekend arrived. It meant that she didn't have to go to school and face her tormentors. Since her mum had been ill, Kirsty had to help with the chores around the house. She would make the beds, dust and clean and generally tidy up. Her mum was getting better now. She could walk around the house but she still needed a wheelchair if she went outside.

It was Saturday afternoon. Kirsty had finished her jobs and she was determined to go for a walk in the park. Once mum was comfortable in her chair, Kirsty put a blanket over her knees and they set off towards Victoria Park. It was cold with a sharp wind, but the sun was shining and, like her mum, Kirsty was well wrapped up.

They stopped near the children's playground. Kirsty recognised the girls immediately. There was Carla showing off on the roundabout and surely that was Yasmin and Simone whizzing her round. Kirsty sat on a park bench next to her mum's wheelchair and wished she could join in with the girls.

'Look who it is!' shouted Yasmin, pointing towards the park bench. 'It's scruffy Kirsty with her mum!'

'What did she say?' asked Kirsty's mum, horrified.

'It doesn't matter,' replied Kirsty, quietly.

The girls whizzed the roundabout faster. Carla was beginning to feel dizzy.

'What's she doing here?' shouted Simone. 'We see enough of her at school!'

'Let me off,' groaned Carla, clinging on to the spinning roundabout for all she was worth. 'I don't feel well!'

'Catch us if you can!' screamed Yasmin, and she gave a final push before she ran off with Simone, pulling a face at Kirsty as she left.

'They're horrible,' said Kirsty's mum. She was obviously upset by the girls' behaviour. 'Why didn't you tell me the girls at your new school were being nasty to you?'

But Kirsty didn't reply. Her eyes were glued to the spinning roundabout and, as she watched, she saw Carla lurch forward with a scream. She was thrown into the air and she landed with a crash on the gravel patch. She immediately yelled with pain and clutched her leg.

'I'll see if she's all right,' said Kirsty, and she set off in Carla's direction.

Carla was clutching her leg and moaning. Her right arm was badly grazed and there was a deep cut above her knee.

'It's O.K.,' said Kirsty, leaning over the injured girl. 'I don't think there's anything broken. Let me help you up. My mum's got a bottle of water in her bag. We can soon clean you up.'

She took hold of Carla's arm and helped her to her feet. Carla wobbled for a moment. She was still a bit dizzy.

'Thanks,' she said, staring hard at Kirsty. 'But I don't understand? Why did you come over to help me? I've been so horrible to you!'

'It doesn't mean to say I've got to be horrible back, does it?' said Kirsty. 'When someone needs help - you don't think about it - you do it!'

'Well, thanks anyway,' said Carla. 'And - I'm really sorry I've been so nasty to you. Maybe we could start again.'

'I'd like that,' said Kirsty with a smile. 'Let's get you sorted out first, should we?'

Prayer: Dear Lord, may we always treat other people as we would want to be treated ourselves. Help us to be kind and considerate. When someone new joins our school or enters our lives, may we welcome them and treat them with respect. Teach us to follow your example and never say or do anything that might cause hurt. Amen.

Follow up: There are many points for discussion. Why were Carla, Simone and Yasmin so horrible to Kirsty? How do you think Kirsty must have felt when she was treated so badly? If you were Kirsty, what would you have done about the situation?

If you were Kirsty would you have helped Carla?

Kirsty was being bullied. She was not physically hurt but she was excluded and she was verbally abused. Stop and think - are you being nasty to anyone? Would you like to be treated in such an appalling way? If you see someone being bullied what should you do about the situation?

Too Helpful Harry

Theme: Giving help when needed

> **Introduction:** Begin by asking the children: 'Has anyone done anything that they would consider helpful recently?' Discuss a couple of the responses. Explain that you really like children who are helpful. There are so many jobs to do around school that reliable and helpful children are a great asset. However, it is possible to try too hard - a little bit like the boy in this story who made a bit of a nuisance of himself by trying to be too helpful.

'Now I want you all to try really hard to be helpful children this week,' explained Mrs Jones, the Headteacher. 'There might just be a special reward at the end of the week for someone who has been particularly helpful.'

Harry had listened intently to the school assembly. He had never really gone out of his way to be particularly helpful but he had made up his mind to make a real effort, especially if there was a chance of a special reward. The problem was - where should he begin?

The first opportunity came at the end of assembly. Someone always held the hall door open so that the children could walk back to class in an orderly manner. Harry took his chance. He pushed his way from his place in the middle of the line and barged towards the hall door, knocking over Emily Richards in his haste to reach the front.

An angry voice boomed out from the front of the hall.

'I saw that Harry! What on earth do you think you are doing?'

Harry froze to the spot and then turned slowly to meet Mrs Jones's glare.

'Just when I'm asking everyone to be helpful you go and cause chaos in the line! You'd better wait at the back of the hall, Harry. You can be the last one out this morning!'

Not a good start. Harry would have to be really helpful for the rest of the week if he was going to get that reward.

Later that morning, as the children were going outside for playtime, Harry's teacher made him hold open the classroom door.

'As you were so eager to help,' said Mrs Hesketh, 'you can be last out to play!'

Harry wasn't pleased. He liked playtimes and he was keen to play football with his classmates. The room was nearly empty when Harry spotted Emily Richards, right at the back of the line.

'Annoying girl!' thought Harry. 'If she hadn't fallen over in the hall I wouldn't have got into trouble!'

Just as Emily was about to leave the room, Harry let go of the door and it swung back and hit Emily in the face. She let out a shriek of pain and immediately burst into tears.

'Harry! How could you?' Mrs Hesketh was not pleased.

'I'm sorry, Mrs Hesketh,' lied Harry. 'It was an accident. The door handle slipped out of my grasp!'

'I hope that's the truth, Harry,' said Mrs Hesketh, putting a comforting arm around Emily. 'You'd better disappear outside before you cause any more trouble.'

Harry was first into the classroom after lunch. He looked around to see if there was any way in which he could be helpful. Ah! Two huge piles of books were stacked at the front of Mrs Hesketh's desk. They were obviously ready to give out to the children. Well, Harry knew where everyone sat. He may as well save the teacher a job. Harry grabbed hold of the first pile and began to give them out. The other children were just coming in as Harry finished the second pile. There was chaos.

'This isn't my book!' protested Emily Richards. Her nose was bruised and swollen.

'And this isn't mine!' said her friend, Dawn.

'They're all wrong!' joined in Andrew Smart. 'Somebody's mixed them all up!'

Mrs Hesketh entered the room and stared in horror. 'What on earth is going on?' she shouted in dismay. 'And who gave all of the exercise books out? I spent ages this lunchtime collecting them from your desks!'

Harry gulped and raised his hand, slowly. 'I was only trying to be helpful,' he stammered. 'Sorry, Mrs Hesketh!'

Harry wasn't very good at cleaning the paint pots. He was always in too much of a hurry. He much preferred to be outside playing football. He was surprised, therefore, when Mrs Hesketh chose him for the job the following lunchtime.

'She obviously thinks I'm really helpful,' thought Harry, and he turned on the tap in the classroom sink and watched as a gush of dark blue paint spilled from the first of the pots. 'Ughh! I'm not putting my fingers in there! It's disgusting!'

Harry grabbed a paintbrush with a large wooden handle and wiggled it about a bit in the pot. The paint was still caked on the bottom of the pot when Harry took it out and turned it upside down on the draining board.

'It's good enough,' he thought. 'She's only going to fill it up again.'
He repeated the process with the rest of the pots until he had reached the last container. By now, the sink was filled with a dark grey sludge as all the paint congealed at the bottom.

'I think Mrs Hesketh will be pleased with this job,' muttered Harry. 'I must say, I've been very helpful.'

He grabbed a paper towel, dried his hands and made his way out of the classroom. Unfortunately, he had forgotten to turn off the tap - and the sink was so full of sludge that it was filling rapidly. Within seconds the filthy liquid was pouring over the top of the sink and flowing onto the classroom floor. Harry whistled to himself as he skipped along the corridor, completely unaware of the disgusting flood that was beginning to engulf the classroom.

130

'I don't believe it!' stormed Mrs Hesketh, as she confronted Harry in the Headteacher's office ten minutes later. Mrs Jones was sitting at her desk looking angry. 'I deliberately gave you a chance to prove yourself, Harry. I can't believe you have let me down so badly!'

Harry opened his mouth to speak but no words came out.

'Don't even try to make an excuse!' stormed Mrs Hesketh. 'Now I want you to help me one more time by promising me something.'

Harry's face brightened in a moment of hope.

'Whatever else you do for the rest of this week, Harry - don't try to be helpful! Do you understand? Do not try to be helpful!'

Prayer: Lord, we know that you are always there to help us and to watch over us. May we always be prepared to give help wherever and whenever it is appropriate. If we are chosen to do a job, give us the common sense to tackle it fully and efficiently. Teach us to be responsible and reliable citizens. Amen.

Follow up: It is easy to feel sorry for Harry - after all, he was only trying to be helpful! However, the story emphasises the importance of responsibility. Stress to the children how important it is to do a job in a responsible and reliable manner. It is sometimes interesting to ask the children themselves who they think, amongst their peers, are responsible and reliable. Explain that teachers always choose children who are responsible and reliable to do their jobs. Discuss the fact that this extends into adult life. Employers want responsible and reliable people to work for them.

Ask the children 'Who helps at home?' Discuss the sort of jobs they do.

Who Will Help the Lion?

Theme: Compassion

> **Introduction:** We all know that it is good to be helpful but there are times, perhaps, when we can be a little selective with our help. For example, if you have a really annoying younger brother or sister at home who asks for help with homework do you agree immediately - even if your favourite programme is on television? If you have squabbled with someone from your class would you rush to help that person if he/she fell over in the playground?
>
> You would not expect a strong lion to need help in the jungle but in this story, lion gets into a spot of bother and help comes from a surprising source.

Lion was in a hurry. He raced through the jungle, dodging tall trees and leaping through the dense undergrowth. He had heard that the hunters were out and he wanted to get home to lioness and their baby lion cubs. Making good progress, he rushed into a clearing and then ground to a halt in suspicion. Something did not feel right; something did not smell right. It was quiet, too. Strangely quiet. Lion crept forward, his great head moving quickly from side to side, scanning the edge of the clearing. Perhaps he was mistaken. He quickened his pace again and then, suddenly, the ground gave way beneath his feet. Lion let out a mighty roar as he tumbled down into the pit - but it was no good - he was well and truly trapped.

What was he to do? The sides were too steep for him to leap out, particularly as he couldn't take a run and jump. Yet if he was to wait for the hunters to return he knew he would never see lioness and his cubs again. There was only one thing for it - he would roar for help and hope that the other animals would come to his rescue. Lion threw back his head and roared for all he was worth. He roared and roared and the mighty sound echoed around the jungle clearing.

Now it happened that snake was slithering by and he heard the distressing sound and recognised lion's roar at once. Filled with curiosity, he glided to the hunter's pit and stared over the edge.

'What s-s-seems to be the matter?' hissed snake, looking in surprise at the trapped lion.

'I'm trapped in the pit,' explained lion. 'You've got to help me out before the hunters return!'

'S-s-sorry,' hissed the snake, backing away. 'I'm not s-s-staying around to be caught by the hunters - but I wish you the best of luck!'

With that the sly snake slid away into the undergrowth leaving lion trapped in the pit.

Some time later, monkey was swinging through the trees when he heard lion's desperate roar. He leapt from the branches and approached the pit.

132

'Mr Lion,' he said, peering over the edge. 'Whatever are you doing down there?'

'I'm trapped in the pit,' repeated the lion. 'You've got to help me out before the hunters return!'

Monkey frowned and took a step backwards. 'Oh, I really don't like pits,' he explained. 'Can't stand enclosed spaces. They make me feel ill. I much prefer the freedom of the trees.' And with that, he leapt for the nearest branch and swung away, chattering.

Lion was getting desperate. Surely it would not be long before the hunters returned. He roared again, not quite so loud, as his throat was becoming sore. To his relief, a small head on the end of a long neck appeared half way down the pit. It was giraffe, on his way to the water hole.

'You've got to help me,' explained lion, for the third time. 'I'm trapped in the pit and the hunters will kill me when they return.'

'Dear, dear, dear!' said the giraffe, withdrawing his neck. 'I'll go and get a drink of water and think about it. I'll be sure to look in on you when I return.' And to lion's disbelief, he disappeared and lolloped off to the water hole.

Poor lion lay on the floor of the pit and put his great paws over his eyes. If neither snake nor monkey nor giraffe would help him he was doomed. He curled up and waited in fear for the hunters to return.

Some considerable time later, there was a snuffling noise near the edge of the pit. Lion leapt to his feet, ready to defend himself against his enemies, the hunters. To his surprise, zebra was peering over the edge. Zebra and lion were not the best of friends. In fact, zebra always steered well clear of lion for fear of being eaten!

'I don't suppose you'd help me?' begged lion, expecting zebra to run off immediately. 'The hunters are sure to kill me when they return.'

'That's true,' said Zebra, staring into the pit in suspicion, 'and you're sure to eat me if I help you out!'

'I won't eat you,' promised lion. 'I'll be your friend forever.'

Zebra stared for a few more moments and then made up his mind. He beat at the ground with his strong hooves until the earth began to loosen and crumble into the hunter's pit. Still he beat at the ground, more and more fiercely, causing the sides of the pit to loosen and collapse completely. Lion leapt onto the mound of crumbling earth and jumped out of the pit with ease. He stood in the jungle clearing and shook his great mane. He moved slowly forward and stared hard at zebra, who backed away in trepidation.

'Thank you, friend,' said lion, his voice trembling with emotion. 'Thank you for saving my life!'

And the two animals turned and raced away over the clearing in opposite directions.

Prayer: May we always be ready, Lord, to help those in need. Teach us that we are all brothers and sisters, whatever our colour or our creed. May we follow your example and be a true friend to everyone. Amen.

Follow up: There are obvious similarities between this story and the parable of The Good Samaritan. Read the Good Samaritan, either in a subsequent assembly or in class and discuss the similarities.

Think of different scenarios that involve a character needing help:
e.g. an old lady falls in the street
a new pupil is all alone in the playgound

List the scenarios on a board/flipchart and ask the children to write a short story about one of them. On completion, share the results with the rest of the class.

Teddy Bears Picnic

Theme: Teddy bears/raising money for charity

Introduction: Why not organise a teddy bears' picnic to raise some money for a good cause? This could be done with one class, a whole Key Stage or the entire school! The event is best held in spring or summer when there is more chance of good weather. Invite the children to pay 50p/£1.00 to bring their favourite teddy bear to school. The bears can be brought into assembly. Encourage staff to bring in a bear! Can you find a version of Teddy Bears' Picnic as they come into the hall? You can choose a few children to talk about their bears. There are many books about bears you can show/read - Paddington, Rupert, Old Bear etc. later in the day, the children could take their bears outside for a picnic and games. (Parents will probably be happy to make some cakes, sandwiches etc.).

The story below is best used a week before the event to stimulate interest.

Mrs Johnson stood at the front of the school hall clutching a battered brown teddy bear.

'What's wrong with her?' whispered Lisa Brown, as the children waited quietly for assembly to begin.

'It's probably stress,' replied Jordan Jones. 'It's been a difficult term.'

The usual introductory music was not playing. Instead, a catchy version of Teddy Bears' Picnic filled the hall. Once the tune had finished, Mrs Johnson took a step forward and said: 'Good morning children!'

'Good morning, Mrs Johnson! Good morning everyone!' chorused the children.

'I think you've forgotten someone!' said Mrs Johnson, holding up the old bear. 'Humphrey would like you to say good morning to him!'

The children giggled immediately.

'She's gone mad!' whispered Lisa.

'Good morning, Humphrey!' chorused the rest of the school.

'Now you're probably wondering why I've brought my teddy bear into assembly this morning,' began Mrs Johnson. 'I've had Humphrey since I was one year old - and that was a very long time ago!'

The Reception Class children nodded in agreement.

'Well, I thought you might like to bring your teddy bears into school and, at the same time, raise some money to help children who are less fortunate than you are. In two weeks time we are going to hold a Teddy Bears Day - complete with our very own Teddy Bears Picnic!'

There was a murmur of approval from the children and some of the staff looked excited.

135

'I'm sure everyone has got a teddy bear at home,' continued Mrs Johnson, 'and if you haven't you will be allowed to bring a guest animal - a sheep or a monkey or another cuddly toy. Who would like to tell me about their teddy bear?'

Holly Higgins from Year 1 shot her hand up into the air.

'My teddy bear's called Gertrude,' she explained seriously. 'She's named after my Grandma.'

'Splendid!' said Mrs Johnson. 'Anyone else?'

To the surprise of the other Year 6 children, Jordan Jones put his hand up.

'My bear's called Cuddles,' he announced seriously. 'It's only got one ear but it's very lovable.'

'You big soft lump!' whispered Lisa Brown.

'My bear is called Ringo,' announced Mr Davies, the Deputy Headteacher. 'He's named after one of The Beatles!'

The children giggled again but Mr Davies didn't seem too bothered.

'I think we are going to have a lovely day,' continued Mrs Johnson. 'Put your hand up if you are going bring your bear into school?'

Every hand shot into the air - including the teachers and the helpers.

'Splendid!' said Mrs Johnson. 'Humphrey and I are looking forward to making some new friends! Make sure your bears get a good night's sleep before they come into school. We don't want them falling asleep in class!'

Jordan nodded seriously. 'Cuddles gets tired easily these days,' he explained to Lisa, who shook her head in disbelief.

'You will all get a letter to take home this evening so that your parents know why we are having a Teddy Bears Day,' continued Mrs Johnson 'and I'll be asking some of them to help with our picnic food. Now, let's continue with our assembly, should we? Humphrey has chosen the hymn this morning and he'd like to sing All Things bright and Beautiful.'

'Good choice,' whispered Jordan. 'Cuddles likes that one!'

Prayer: Lord, thank you for the small things in life that bring us pleasure and enjoyment. It is sometimes easy to forget just how much we have and how lucky we are. May we remember those children who are less fortunate than ourselves and may we do all we can to help make their lives easier. Amen.

Follow up: Ask the children to look for stories about bears. The stories can then be shared in class on the lead up to Teddy Bears Day.

The children could plan and write their own stories. It would be good for the older children to write and illustrate their own books which could be read to the younger ones on the Teddy Bears Day.

When did teddy bears first appear? Get the children to research the history of teddy bears.

George and the Ladder

Theme: Common sense

Introduction: Explain to the children that as well as learning lessons at school, the teachers try to encourage them to be responsible citizens who have a great deal of common sense. Common sense is not a National Curriculum subject but it is important if you are to succeed in life. You can not really teach it but you can encourage and promote common sense. For example, it is common sense not to push and shove in the dinner queue; it is common sense not to play in puddles when it has been raining. Can anyone think of another example?

You can learn a lot from today's story by not behaving like the main character who seemed to have no common sense at all!

From the moment he had been able to speak, George was one of those children who showed little common sense. As a baby he would sit in his high chair and smack his food with his plastic spoon so that it splattered everywhere - mostly all over him! He would try to climb out of his cot and invariably fall onto the floor and hurt himself. But did he learn from his mistake? No - once replaced, he would climb over the side and fall again.

As he grew older, he got worse. If there was a puddle in the road, George would jump in it, soaking himself and anybody else nearby. On one occasion he bounced up and down on his bed, using it like a trampoline - until he bounced so high that he cracked his head on the ceiling. That was a trip to the hospital for stitches.

At school, when it was the games lesson, no one managed to be more covered in mud than George. He even seemed to get muddy when it had not been raining. George would walk home covered from head to foot and then collapse onto the sofa until his mother screamed at him to take a shower.

His lack of common sense seemed even more noticeable when he was a teenager. On one occasion, his mum sent him to the fishmongers. Mr Jarvis, the fishmonger, told him to keep the fish under refrigeration and so George stuffed it under the fridge when he got home. It was only the awful smell in the kitchen the following morning that gave his blunder away.

It was soon after that mistake that George had an awful day. His mum had never left him alone at home for more than a few hours but when her sister was taken ill, she decided to spend a few days with her. She was a bit worried as to how George would cope but he had to learn sooner or later.

'Now don't do anything daft,' she warned. 'Use your common sense. Make sure the fire's turned off at night and if you go out keep the key somewhere safe. I don't want to come home to any disasters!'

137

'No problem,' said George, confidently. 'I'll use my common sense.'

Everything was fine for the first hour and then George decided to go down to the local shop for some sweets. He put on his jacket, locked the back door and then collected the house key from the dish in the hallway. He remembered his mother's words: 'If you go out keep the key somewhere safe.' George set the burglar alarm and left the house, locking the door behind him.

He stopped on the front path and stared at the house key. 'Hmmm somewhere safe!' he thought. 'I know! I'll post it through the letter box. It will be perfectly safe in the house because I've locked the door!' And he slipped the key through the letter box and listened in satisfaction as it rattled on the floor. 'Mum would be pleased with me,' he thought. 'I've used my common sense!'

Ten minutes later, George stood on the front path with a bag of sweets in his hand and stared at the locked door. 'Bit of a problem . . .' he said to himself, scratching his head. 'Never mind, I'll just have to use my common sense.' And then he had an idea. It was as if a light bulb had been switched on. 'There's a ladder in the shed,' he said aloud. 'I'll climb in through the bathroom window! No problem!'

George went round to the back of the house and down to the garden shed. There was a spare key for the shed hidden beneath a stone and George soon had the ladder on the back lawn. George looked up at the bathroom window and then he stared at the ladder. It looked a bit short. Never mind, he could scramble up the drainpipe if it didn't quite reach the window.

He placed the ladder against the wall and began to climb. It was well short - and George didn't like heights. His knees were knocking together. He reached across and grabbed hold of the drainpipe but as he did so, the ladder moved and began to slide. George let out a yell as it crashed to the ground, leaving him hanging from the drainpipe.

'Keep calm!' he said to himself. 'Keep calm!'

Somehow he managed to scramble up the pipe onto the narrow window ledge. He dared not look down. The window looked a bit small but with one last effort, George hoisted himself up and into the gap. It was so tight! He wriggled and squirmed until he was half way through - and then - disaster! George had forgotten about the intruder alarm. The bathroom sensor picked up his movement and the alarm suddenly screamed. To make matters worse, George was well and truly stuck. He was wedged into the window and he couldn't move! His front half was in the bathroom and his legs and backside were sticking out of the window!

It took the fire brigade and the police to set George free. The ambulance had arrived, too, just in case he needed attention.

'What on earth were you doing?' asked an incredulous police officer once George had recovered.

'I was just using my common sense,' explained George. 'I didn't mean any harm!'

The following day, when George's mother arrived home, she knew nothing of the disaster.

'Everything all right, dear?' she asked, as she entered the house, smiling.

'Nothing to report?'

'Everything's been fine,' lied George, limping into the hallway to meet her. 'You can go away from home any time you wish. There hasn't been a problem!'

Prayer: Dear Lord, give us the common sense to make the right choices in life, especially when we are faced with difficult decisions. Help us to grow up to be kind and considerate people who will always do a good turn for others. May we follow your example and be guided by your teaching. Amen.

Follow up: Encourage the children to think positively about each other and to take responsibility for their own actions. At the end of the week, ask them to nominate a member of class who has displayed common sense. The children should give a reason for their choice.

Discuss other situations in school that require common sense.

Butterfly Summer

Theme: Butterflies/Nature

Introduction: Explain to the children that we share our world with thousands of other creatures. Sometimes humans are very selfish and damage the natural environment. For example, a new motorway may cut across the countryside destroying natural habitat; an area of open land might be sold off for housing; a wood or forest might be cleared for development. In some parts of the world, natural rainforests are being destroyed and many species are becoming endangered. People should be more aware of the wonderful variety of creatures that make up our world and sometimes this can start in a very small way.

It was the first day of the summer holiday and Yasmin was helping her mum in the back garden. The sun was shining from a clear blue sky and, although it was quite early in the morning, Yasmin was already feeling hot.

'Can we have a drink?' she asked. 'I'm really thirsty.'

'We've only been working for fifteen minutes!' laughed mum. 'Go on, then! You go in and get us a cold drink and I'll finish this bit of weeding.'

A few minutes later, Yasmin and her mum were sitting on the wooden bench at the bottom of the garden enjoying a cold drink of fresh orange. It was great to be off school. The family were going on holiday to the coast in another couple of weeks. Yasmin couldn't wait.

Just as Yasmin was finishing her drink, a bright colourful butterfly flew over the fence from next door's garden and landed on a tall purple plant.

'Look!' said Yasmin, pointing towards the delicate creature. 'It's lovely! What is it?'

'It's a butterfly,' replied Yasmin's mum, surprised at the question.

Yasmin gave her a withering look. 'I know it's a butterfly but the colours are lovely. What type is it?'

Yasmin's mum got up slowly to take a closer look. The butterfly was lovely. It was probably only about five or six centimetres in width but its wings were beautifully coloured and paterned. It was very dark, almost black with a band of deep red crossing each wing. Further along towards the tips of the wings were a series of white markings. Yasmin walked over quietly to join her mum and the two of them stood and watched as the butterfly took off and fluttered across the garden to another plant.

'I think it's a Red Admiral,' said mum, as they turned to follow the creature. 'You'd have to look it up in the library to be sure. When I was a little girl there used to be a lot more butterflies around the gardens.'

Yasmin looked puzzled. 'I don't understand,' she said. 'Why were there more butterflies when you were a little girl?'

'People didn't use chemical sprays as much in those days,' explained mum, 'and there wasn't as much traffic on the road polluting the atmosphere.'

The Red Admiral took off again and disappeared into the next garden.

'Did you notice how the pattern was exactly the same on each wing?' said Yasmin's mum. 'That's called symmetrical.'

'I know about symmetry,' said Yasmin, 'we've learnt about it at school.'

'There are still a good number of butterflies around,' said mum, 'but we need to look after them. They're more attracted to certain plants, such as that purple buddleia or the little hebe in the border.'

Yasmin's mum pointed to a small, round shrub and to Yasmin's delight, there was another butterfly hovering near the flowers. This time it was a yellowish white colour with just a hint of green. Yasmin didn't think it was quite as attractive as the Red Admiral but she was interested, nevertheless.

'I know that one,' said Yasmin's mum. 'It's called a Brimstone butterfly. Its caterpillars are bright green in colour.'

'I wonder why they're called butterflies?' said Yasmin. 'What have they got to do with butter?'

'Some people say it's because a lot of them are yellowish in colour,' said Yasmin's mum. 'But there are so many lovely colours I'm not sure.'

'How long do butterflies live?' asked Yasmin, moving closer.

'It depends what type they are,' answered mum. 'Butterflies can live for about a year. Of course, butterflies like hot, sunny days. They're very sensible creatures - they hibernate in winter.'

'I'm going to find out more about them,' said Yasmin. 'I'll go to the library and get a book out about butterflies and I'll start my very own note and sketch book. I'll keep a watch to see how many different types visit our garden and I'll try to draw a picture of each one.'

'What a good idea,' said mum. 'And we can find out about other plants that attract butterflies. We'll make our garden butterfly friendly.'

'And when we go on holiday to the seaside I'll see if there are any different types of butterfly,' said Yasmin.

'Yes,' agreed mum, 'I think we'll have a butterfly summer, should we?'

'Butterfly summer,' repeated Yasmin. 'That's what I'll put on the front of my note and sketch book. Butterfly summer!'

Prayer: Thank you, Lord, for our wonderful world. Sometimes humans are selfish and think only of themselves. Help us to appreciate that we share our world with a variety of creatures. May we do all we can to protect and encourage wildlife and may we be conscious to look after our environment so that it can be enjoyed by future generations. Amen.

Follow up: The children could use the school library or search the Internet to produce illustrated factsheets about butterflies. Alternately, a homework task could be set to design and present an A4 factsheet about butterflies.

141

A class or group of children could conduct a butterfly survey in the school grounds or local environment. Obviously, a warm sunny day would provide the best results. The children could be organised into pairs or small groups. On return to class, they could try to identify the different butterflies observed.

Is your school butterfly friendly? Is there a patch of school garden that could be planted to encourage wildlife - especially butterflies?